WEDDING ANNOUNCEMENT

Stacy Larson, née Ernshaw,
announces her wedding to
Mr. Royke Larson.

Married at a lovely, run-down
chapel in Las Vegas,
the quickie ceremony was
witnessed by hired strangers.
Family and friends were not present.

Well-wishes may be sent to
the happy couple at the
Larson Ranch.

Please address questions and book requests to: Silhouette Reader Service
U.S.: 3010 Walden Ave., P.O. Box 1325, Buffalo, NY 14269
Canadian: P.O. Box 609, Fort Erie, Ont. L2A 5X3

Hitched in Haste

WESTERN *Lovers*™

JOAN HOHL

SOMEONE WAITING

Silhouette Books

Published by Silhouette Books
America's Publisher of Contemporary Romance

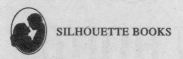 SILHOUETTE BOOKS

ISBN 0-373-30160-X

SOMEONE WAITING

This edition published by arrangement with Harlequin Books S.A.

® and TM are trademarks of Harlequin Books S.A., used under license. Trademarks indicated with ® are registered in the United States Patent and Trademark Office, the Canadian Trade Marks Office and in other countries.

Visit Silhouette at www.eHarlequin.com

Printed in U.S.A.

For Bonnie Wenger—
I lose count of the times I've given thanks
for the night I went to visit a neighbor
and found a dear friend.

Chapter One

Stacy should have considered the assignment
a plum. She did not. On the contrary, she
thought it a drag. Just what the reading public
needs, she groaned silently. Yet another article on the drudgery faced by the average
American housewife!

Carefully placing a neatly folded shirt into
her open suitcase, Stacy frowned in concentration. Had she forgotten anything? After a
swift mental check, she shrugged slightly
then proceeded to tie the restraining ribbons
before closing the valise with a click of fi-

nality. She had a job to do and, like it or not, she would do it.

"Dinner is on the table, Stacy."

Virginia Ernshaw's precise English deepened the frown marring Stacy's brow. There were times when Stacy longed to hear just one ungrammatical sentence from her mother. Of course, Stacy was all too aware that the chances of having her longing fulfilled were slim. Virginia Ernshaw did not play the role of English professor; she lived it each and every day of her life!

"Coming." Casting a rueful glance around the room, Stacy swung through the door and along the hall to the dining room as if she were striding on air. Her mother *did* think the assignment a plum. Stacy lacked the fortitude needed to disagree with her.

As Stacy entered the room Virginia paused in the act of tossing the salad to glance up at her daughter expectantly.

"Everything in order, dear?"

Stacy recognized the question for exactly what it was—rhetorical. She knew that were she to answer, "Actually, everything's a mess," her mother would stare at her as if she'd suddenly gone berserk. There wasn't a thing that would dare to be disordered in Virginia's neatly arranged life.

"As much in order as possible, I suppose," Stacy responded distractedly, seating herself at the table. "Apparently there's no second-guessing the early spring weather in Montana." She removed her napkin from the smooth wooden ring, shook it gently, and draped it across her lap. "I've tried to anticipate every conceivable contingency, but..." She lifted her slim shoulders in a helpless shrug.

"Since you are going to be there only a few days at best, I would think boots, jeans, serviceable shirts, and a warm jacket would suffice," Virginia declared with her usual practicality. "You are going to that godforsaken place on assignment, not on a social jaunt."

Stacy quelled a burst of laughter. Did her mother think she was off to the back of beyond? Hiding a smile behind a forkful of salad, she supplied the answer—yes, Virginia really did think her daughter was going into the hinterlands! Any place beyond a fifty-mile radius of a metropolitan area was considered the boonies by Virginia and her cronies.

"And what do I do if my host and hostess dress for dinner?" The query was made sweetly, and with tongue in cheek. Stacy hadn't even considered the possibility of a ranch family donning bib and tucker before sitting down to supper. She had posed the question simply to needle her mother—just a tiny bit. But the needle turned to prick Stacy's own conscience. Was she being snobbish herself? Did ranch families dress for dinner? Stacy gave herself a mental shake; it was too late to worry over now, when her suitcase was packed and locked. Not at all surprisingly, Virginia took the question seriously.

"I hardly think you need concern yourself over that particular contingency, Stacy." Virginia's condescending tone grated on Stacy's already raw nerves; she really did not want this assignment! "A working ranch," Virginia droned on pedantically, "is a working ranch, after all."

How extraordinarily profound! Stacy swallowed the exclamation along with the bite of lamb chop she'd been chewing to smithereens; she didn't really want the chop, either. Her private annoyance with her mother's generalizations was occurring a lot more frequently of late. Why *was* she so very discontented with everything and everybody? As no answer presented itself, Stacy ignored her lamb chop and attacked the steaming baked potato alongside it on her plate.

"Don't gulp your food, dear."

Stacy's teeth came together with a muffled click. It was one month past Stacy's twenty-fifth birthday and Virginia was still speaking to her as if she were twelve! That is, Stacy qualified, when she isn't expecting me to display the maturity of fifty! How does Mother resolve the contradiction in her own mind? Stacy wondered, not for the first time. More to the point, how the devil does she expect *me* to resolve the contradiction? Stacy gathered her wandering thoughts and concentrated on Virginia's lecture-hall drone.

"...shouldn't take more than a few days at most."

Stacy had to assume Virginia was referring to her trip to Montana. The instructions that followed proved her assumption correct.

"I have stocked the freezer, so you will have more than enough food to tide you over till I get back." Virginia's face glowed with excitement. "I am really looking forward to this cruise!"

To say nothing of the man you'll be sailing with, Stacy thought wearily. How many men had passed through her mother's life since her father's death five years before? Slowly chewing whatever it was she'd put into her mouth, Stacy paraded the men through her mind. First there had been that Dave something-or-other; Stacy hadn't liked him at all— possibly because he'd entered her life, and her mother's bedroom, less than a year after her father died. Then there'd been George of the silver hair and matching tongue. Stacy personally wouldn't have trusted *him* as far as she could throw him! Grant Parker followed George. There was a man after Stacy's own heart! Tall, quiet, capable...too capable for Virginia's taste! Virginia *did* enjoy feeling superior. Now, during the spring break at the university, she was going cruising with number four, one James Mallory, a man after *Virginia's* own heart! Stacy repressed a sigh. Oh, well, the rather vague but sweet professor of English literature was probably the perfect mate for Virginia, if such an animal existed.

"Stacy!" Virginia said sharply. "I asked you a question."

Stacy blinked. "I'm sorry, Mother. I was, ah, thinking."

"Indeed?" Virginia frowned. "Are you feeling quite right? You have been acting strange lately."

"Yes, Mother, I feel fine." Stacy produced a smile as proof. "What was the question?"

"I asked if you have plans for this evening?"

"No." Stacy shook her head briefly. "Why?"

"Because James is coming over." Virginia's still beautiful face revealed nothing, yet Stacy somehow knew there was more to come. Stacy was right on target. "His nephew has been staying with him for a few days." There was a slight pause. "James is bringing him along to meet you."

This time Stacy was not altogether successful in smothering a groan. Wonderful! And just what she needed at this particular moment! Why was her mother suddenly intent on pairing her up with a man? Was the relationship between Virginia and James getting serious? Perhaps, Stacy mused, her mother was trying to ease her out the door by the age-old method of easing her into the care of a husband!

"I wanted to get to bed early, Mother!" Stacy protested. "My plane is scheduled to depart at seven-forty."

"I am well aware of your schedule, Stacy," Virginia snapped. "For that matter, so is James." With her customary brisk efficiency Virginia began clearing the table. "They will not stay very long. James simply wanted you to meet his nephew." With the dish-laden tray in her hands, she paused in the archway to the kitchen to glance back at her daughter reprovingly. "His name is Bradley, by the way, since you haven't asked. I think you'll like him. He is a very nice young man."

With sweaty palms clasped together tightly in her lap, Stacy sat rigidly in the narrow seat, swallowing repeatedly in an effort to contain the tide of nausea rising in her constricted throat. No matter how many times she told herself it was ridiculously childish, Stacy faced every airplane flight with abject terror. Desperately hoping to escape by falling asleep, she rested her head against the high seat back and closed her eyes. Sleep was elusive, but Stacy did manage to distract herself by recalling the events of the evening before and her meeting with Bradley Mallory.

Surprisingly, Virginia's observation had proved correct. Stacy did indeed like Brad, for he obviously was a very nice young man, well-mannered and polite...and not bad to look at, either!

At five foot nine, Brad seemed to tower over Stacy's petite five-foot-three, fashionably slender frame. His hair was sandy brown, wavy, and squeaky clean. His eyes were bright blue, and sparkled with good humor. His facial features were well put together. His smile was sweet and boyishly engaging. He left Stacy completely cold.

Sighing quietly, Stacy shifted into a more comfortable position. She really had liked Brad, but she felt not the slightest attraction

to him. When Virginia and James slipped
away into the kitchen, ostensibly to get re-
freshments, Stacy had not felt even one tiny
flutter of excitement at being alone with Brad.
What she had felt was amusement at Virginia
and James and their obvious ploy.

Now, after reflection, Stacy's amusement
turned sour. Brad was the third young man in
as many months that her mother had trotted
before her. In fact, she thought grumpily, she
was beginning to feel like the only mare on
a stud farm! What *was* Virginia hoping for?
A scenario from the pages of a fairy tale? The
slam-bam-alakasam of love at first sight for
Stacy and one of these "nice young men"?

A bittersweet smile touched Stacy's softly
curved lips. If that was what her mother
hoped for, then the whole thing was pretty
ironic. Virginia had never even allowed Stacy
to read fairy tales! For as long as Stacy could
remember, Virginia had preached the hard
line of the militant feminists to her. Stacy had
grown up well versed on all the rights due to
women. As rebelliousness had never been one
of the ingredients in her personal makeup,

Stacy had accepted her mother's schooling without question.

Upwardly mobile—the catch phrase had become Stacy's motto. All through her school years, from nursery school through college, Stacy had striven to achieve. She had earned her degree with a solid 4.0 average. Diploma in hand, she had followed her mother's suggestion to apply for a position as junior reporter for a small bimonthly publication called *Women First*.

Shifting again in the cramped confines of her seat, Stacy grimaced at the recollection of her interview with the founder and editor of the magazine.

"I would have known you were Virginia's daughter without any introduction." Rising from her chair behind a very cluttered desk, Toni Franklin had extended her small hand as Stacy crossed the space from the door to her desk. As Toni gripped Stacy's hand she destroyed all Stacy's hopes of making her own way in the business world. "I spoke to Virginia less than fifteen minutes ago. Your scholastic record is very impressive, especially the work you did on the campus paper. The job is yours...if you want it.''

So much for independence!

The pattern had been set; Stacy took the job.

Nonetheless, she knew that what she'd achieved on the job was due solely to her own initiative. At twenty-two Stacy had started her career as a glorified gofer. Then came the minor interviews—during which she'd sometimes been carried away by her own enthusiasm. Now, at twenty-five, Stacy knew she was considered fair but ruthlessly single-minded while working on an article or story. She was also considered one of the best, and had acquired a small but vocal following. Her contributions had enhanced a magazine already well known for articles featuring some of the most recognizable names of the women's movement. In all honesty Stacy knew she had reason to be proud of her work.

Stacy bit back a gasp as her stomach muscles clenched again. This time the feeling of nausea was not caused by the realization that she was riding thousands of feet in the air in a very heavy jet plane held aloft, as she was firmly convinced, by her prayers and the knowledge of a relatively small number of men with the brilliant understanding of aerodynamics. No, this particular type of pain and nausea had become a near constant with Stacy of late. It had begun as a mildly irritating burning sensation some two months previously and had slowly escalated to a full-fledged fire within the last week and a half.

Pressure. Stress. Nerves.

Stacy had blamed all three as the cause for her discomfort. Telling herself that all she needed was a rest, she had not taken the time to consult a doctor. The opportunity for a vacation had not materialized. The frequency of the attacks increased.

Stacy breathed with slow regularity as the plane started its descent for a short layover in Chicago. But when finally the plane sat motionless on the runway, Stacy's breathing was far from calm. At the announcement that their ground time would be approximately one hour, she joined the line of deplaning passengers. After exchanging a few hurried words with the young male flight attendant, Stacy

strode along the enclosed boarding ramp in
quest of a ladies' room and a glass of milk.

She might as well have taken her time, for
she had rushed only to stand in a long line at
both the rest room and the refreshment
counter. After swallowing the soothing contents of a small, expensive container of milk,
she gathered her courage together to face the
remainder of the flight. Chewing methodically on two antacid tablets, she walked
briskly back to the departure lounge, telling
herself it was absolutely juvenile to hope the
plane had taken off without her. She had a
job to do and, come hell, high water, or a fire
in her stomach, she would do it!

Stacy was one of the last to board, and as
she walked down the aisle she noticed that
the large jet was now less than half full.
Though she probably could have seated herself anywhere, she slid into the seat assigned
to her at the outset of her journey. On the first
leg of her flight she had been flanked by two
men, neither of whom she'd noticed beyond
the fact that they were men. Now the aisle
seat was empty, and there was a different man
at the window. Stacy knew the man was dif-

ferent by simple deduction. The first passenger to occupy the window seat had done so in relative comfort. The man seated beside her now seemed at a loss as to what to do with his long legs.

Surreptitiously observing the movement of his well-muscled thighs encased in fine wool slacks, Stacy was unaware of the passage of time until the jet began slowly taxiing to its designated runway. There was a flurry of activity beside her, and then the muscular thighs were partially concealed by a large attaché case.

As the whine of the engines grew louder, the lid of the case rose and a long-fingered hand, sparsely covered with a sprinkling of short dark hairs, delved into its contents. The fingers retrieved a blue folder, and then the case was closed with a firm snap. As if the click of the small lock were the awaited-for signal, the plane began racing down the strip, and Stacy's hands grasped the armrests on either side of her seat.

Muscular thighs, long fingers, and blue folders fled from Stacy's mind. Swallowing convulsively, she closed her eyes. Sleep.

Stacy's conscious order to her subconscious mind was ignored. Then think. What about? Anything. Something. The state of the economy. The state of your bank balance. The state of Montana. Anything that will blank out the thought of soaring thousands of feet above the earth!

Montana. Her assignment. It was the last place in the world Stacy would have chosen to go. Did anything ever happen in Montana? Yet the circumstances surrounding the setting up of this interview still amazed Stacy.

"How in the world did you ever find this Sandi Case?" she'd asked Toni incredulously.

"Through one of those stranger-than-fiction occurrences." Toni grinned impishly, taking full advantage of her gamine appearance. But Stacy was long past being taken in by Toni's little-girl looks; she knew too well that beneath Toni's innocent facade beat a heart of pure steel. "A few weeks ago," Toni continued, "I received a rather scathing letter from a woman near Billings, Montana. It seems this woman had picked up a copy of *Women First* while waiting for her child in a dentist's office.'' Here Toni paused to smile wryly. ''The dentist was a woman,'' she drawled before continuing with her explanation. ''In any case, our letter-writer was apparently incensed by our magazine's bias.''

''Bias?'' Stacy asked.

''Mmm,'' Toni nodded sagely. ''And I quote—'' at this point Toni fished a sheet of paper from her cluttered desk '''—What an absolutely biased publication! Every one of the articles was written about, and obviously for, the professional woman. Is the editorial staff aware of the fact that there are women in this country who have chosen to remain at home?''' Toni rolled her eyes ceilingward. ''There's more—'' she waved the piece of plain stationery ''—a lot more. But our writer concludes by mentioning the example of a friend, one Sandi Case, a *professional* housewife...and all-around paragon.'' Now Toni contrived to look sinister. ''I personally called our correspondent's bluff by calling her on the phone and asking her if she could arrange an interview for us with her friend the paragon.''

"And?" Stacy prompted when Toni again paused.

"Surprise, surprise! She not only agreed to talk to her friend, she pulled it off—" Toni tilted her head at Stacy "—one Stacy Ernshaw, to stay at the Case ranch while working on the article."

"How lucky can one reporter get?" Stacy had sighed.

Lucky indeed! Here she was, feeling the telltale signs of an ulcer, battling airsickness, on her way to a ranch in the middle of nowhere.

Why the hell do I continue to do it?

Coming from deep within her subconscious mind, the thought startled Stacy so much she jerked erect in the narrow seat, bumping the arm of the man sitting next to her in the process. With a mumbled "I beg your pardon," she settled back again and closed her eyes, not even bothering to look at the man when he made a softly voiced reply.

"No harm done."

Why had the thought popped into her mind? Stacy demanded of herself. She loved her work...didn't she? The now familiar burning pain joined forces with the airsickness. Oh, God! Stacy felt terrible. Would this flight never end? But, she groaned silently, even when it did end, her ordeal would not be over. She would then have to rush onto a smaller connecting plane for the last leg of her journey.

Why had the errant thought popped into her mind? Stacy examined the possibilities. Sure, she'd grown slightly disenchanted with the same old party line. To no one but herself would Stacy admit that hearing the subjects of her interviews expound at length about equality had become a bore. Lord! Were there no other topics? Stacy personally felt as strongly about equal rights for women as the women she interviewed, but that didn't mean she wanted to discuss the topic to the exclusion of everything else!

Feeling somewhat disloyal, Stacy squirmed uncomfortably in the confining seat. Why did she have this vague sensation of discontent lately? By rights she should be feeling on top of the world. She'd earned recognition in her field, and a generous salary because of it. She was healthy—at least she had been until recently—she was reasonably attractive, and she was heart-free. So then, why wasn't she deliriously happy? Or, at that rate, even mildly so?

Heart-free. The phrase lingered to trouble Stacy. Was that her problem? Was she emotionally starved? In the deepest part of her being was she yearning for someone, some one man, to love? Was she longing to *be* loved? Stacy sighed, wondering what loving and being loved by a man to the exclusion of all else would be like. Could love like that exist? Never having been in love, Stacy had no basis for an answer, but she strongly suspected that the kind of overwhelming emotion that one read about in books, and heard about in songs, lived only in the fertile imaginations of authors and composers. Surely, Stacy reasoned, if that deep, romantic, all-consuming emotion existed, she would have stumbled across it by now.

The fire in Stacy's middle shot sparks up into her chest and, stifling a groan, she opened her eyes, then quickly shut them again when her ears popped. The plane was beginning to descend. The very last thing Stacy wanted to see was the earth rushing to meet her and, from experience, she knew that unless she kept her eyes tightly closed, her glance would be drawn inexorably to the window and the terrain below.

Finally, the plane stood motionless again and Stacy allowed herself a heaving sigh of relief before scurrying out of her seat. She had to dash to make her connection.

It immediately became obvious that some of her fellow passengers had to make the same connection, for several men went striding past her in the concourse, their destination the same commuter line that she was heading for. The call to board came as the attendant marked Stacy's flight folder. One good thing, Stacy mused glumly, her heels clicking on the cement as she hurried toward the small commuter plane, she hadn't had time to become even more nervous…if it were possible to become more nervous than she was already!

Beginning to feel as if she'd been in the air forever, Stacy went into her detachment routine as the prop plane lifted off the ground and climbed into the sky…but not too high into the sky, Stacy realized sickly.

Now, what had she been thinking about? Oh, yes. Oh, God! Stacy's eyes flew wide open as the plane shuddered through some turbulence. Carefully avoiding the window, she glanced down, then frowned. Was that not the same pair of legs she'd observed shifting around earlier? It was. Apparently Long Legs was on his way to the same place she was. Stacy shrugged. The turbulence over, she forced her fingers to release their clutching grasp on the armrests and she once again closed her eyes.

Love. Ha! In Stacy's opinion, love was a polite word used to describe plain old carnal desire. And marriage was merely the accepted prerequisite of procreation—and even *that* prerequisite was losing ground. Unless she was seeing all the wrong people, Stacy decided, she had never witnessed real, true love. Practically everyone Stacy knew was either on their second or third marriage or lover, or both, her own mother included. Stacy's father had not been Virginia's first husband. Virginia had readily admitted to Stacy that she had mistakenly married her high school sweetheart directly upon graduation—and had divorced him during her junior year of college.

Was this love? If it was, Stacy wanted no part of it. In actual fact, Stacy had had no part of it. Cautious to the bone, Stacy, at the ripe old age of twenty-five, was still a virgin. And Stacy was beginning to believe she'd remain a virgin forever! Brad had not been the first man to leave Stacy cold. Every man left Stacy cold. Where was the man who could melt her bones with a look, or create fireworks with his kiss? Stacy had given up hope of meeting that man long ago. And, unless she could have melting bones and fireworks, she simply was not interested in playing at the game of love.

All of which introspection did not answer the question: Was she emotionally starved? Very likely, Stacy conceded wryly. I might as well add sexually frustrated, too. How often had she heard the expression ''she needs a man'' used in reference to a restless, irritable woman? More times than she cared to remember, but then, the observation was usually voiced by a man. All the same, in Stacy's own case perhaps it was true! Maybe sexual repression was the cause of her restlessness *and* her stomach disorder!

At that point in her conjecturing Stacy's ears popped and her stomach performed an imitation of a half gainer. The little plane was descending—and shuddering. Her throat closing with fear, Stacy gripped the armrests with sweaty hands. Oh, God! Was the plane going to crash?

"Steady."

His voice was low and calm. Still more reassuring was the feel of his long-fingered hand, which covered the back of Stacy's trembling fingers.

"Are..." Stacy swallowed against the boulder in her throat. "Are we going to crash?"

"Of course not." The low voice was confidence-inspiring; the long fingers tightened reassuringly on hers. "It's a bit windy, that's all. Relax, we'll be down in a moment."

Stacy opened her eyes and felt her bones begin to melt. There was nothing extraordinary about his face. In fact, it was rather rough-hewn and craggy. His eyes were brown, just plain dark brown, but intelligent and intense. Fortunately for Stacy, who had the uncanny sensation that they could appear very distant when he was angry, they were filled with compassion at that moment. His lips were sharply, almost cruelly sculpted, but now the sharpness was softened by a gentle smile.

"There," the low voice purred as the wheels touched down. "All over now."

Embarrassed and still quaking inside, Stacy blurted out the first thing that sprang to her mind. "I'm sorry, I'm such a fool when it comes to flying."

"There's no reason to apologize. Many people fear flying."

"I—I know." Stacy smiled deprecatingly. "But I do so hate being one of them."

The plane came to a stop and Stacy's hand was released. Wondering at the sudden coolness in her fingers, she flipped open her seat belt and stood up. As she stepped into the aisle she glanced down at the dark-haired, dark-eyed man.

"Thank you," she murmured before hurrying to the exit.

Chapter Two

You're welcome.

Royke Larson had not spoken the words aloud. The smile faded from his hard, rather thin lips as he ran his gaze over the young woman's back. His eyes traveled slowly from the top of her short, curly, chestnut-colored hair to the tips of her expensive, totally useless knee-high leather boots. The equally expensive, muted-gold suede suit she was wearing hugged her slender figure to advantage. Royke's smile reappeared momentarily...to his advantage!

A beauty. A real honest-to-goodness natu-

ral beauty. Not too tall, Royke judged. Some-
where in the neighborhood of five foot three
or four and, with what he'd glimpsed of her
proportions, that was some classy neighborhood!

Who is she? he mused, getting to his feet
carefully; Royke had learned long ago to
move slowly when rising from the narrow
confines of a plane.

Finally standing to his full six foot height
in the now empty aisle, Royke collected his
raincoat from the tiny compartment then
scooped up his attaché case. A few long
strides carried him to the exit. Murmuring a
terse "thank you" to the attendant, he tipped
his head to clear the low opening. Not un-
appreciative of the speculative glance the uni-
formed blonde sent gliding over his length,
he let a wisp of a smile play at the corners of
his mouth as he loped down the steps and
along the yellow-lined walk to the small terminal. The blonde was forgotten the moment
the door closed behind him. Not so the chestnut beauty.

Who was she?

Royke frowned with impatience. Chances

were he'd never set eyes on her again. Why should he even bother wondering about her? He had more important things to wonder about, mainly whether the rental service had a car ready for him as arranged, and how long he'd have to cool his heels waiting for his suitcase to be unloaded. Royke had been away from home for nearly two weeks; he was eager to get back to the ranch.

Striding into the baggage-claim area, he frowned more deeply. Every one of the passengers from the flight he'd been on, as well as passengers from at least two other flights, were milling around waiting for luggage that hadn't even begun to appear on the baggage belt.

Ignoring his own earlier advice, Royke scanned the faces of the restless people, searching for a particularly lovely, piquantly vulnerable countenance.

Vulnerable?

Royke's eyes narrowed as he considered the description. Yes, she had appeared vulnerable and, for some reason, he felt positive that her air of vulnerability had little to do with her terror of flying. While his eyes continued to probe the crowd, Royke called to mind a picture of her as she had appeared the first time he'd noticed her.

She had boarded the plane in Chicago, projecting an image of cool composure. Disdaining her surroundings, she had not bothered to look at her fellow passengers, let alone acknowledge them. Even then Royke's eyes had been busy taking her measure…and measurements!

From the moment she'd buckled her delectably slender body into the seat next to his, Royke had casually studied her, catching every nuance as her demeanor changed from composure to barely suppressed terror. In sympathy, he had observed her tightly clasped hands, the moisture that beaded her forehead, and the gallant effort she'd made to escape through sleep. Then the minute the plane's wheels touched ground, she'd become the supremely confident woman again. Yet, even then Royke had sensed that air of vulnerability about her. Strange… Royke shook his head in perplexity. He knew many beautiful and interesting women. What was it about this particular young woman that stirred all kinds of reactions inside his mind and body?

Unable to locate the only face in the crowd that held any interest for him, Royke swung his gaze back to the baggage belt, biting back a curse when he found it still devoid of luggage. Lord! It was beginning to look like collecting his suitcase was going to take almost as long as the entire trip had!

"Royke?"

Royke turned slowly at the sound of the familiar voice calling his name, a smile softening the severity of his lips.

"Hi, Sandi!" Royke's naturally deep voice held a lilt of surprise. "What are you doing here? Coming, going, or meeting?"

"Meeting." Sandi flashed a grin. "That reporter from Philadelphia. Remember?"

Remember? Royke grimaced. How could he forget? Hadn't he spent the major part of one evening trying to talk Sandi out of doing this proposed interview? He had, and he'd nearly talked himself hoarse for nothing. Sandi had started out and ended up adamant. Once committed, she always saw a project through to completion. As a rule, Royke ad-

mired Sandi's tenacity, but in this instance he
was convinced she was making a mistake.
Sandi led a full, busy life. The last thing she
needed was a strident, condescending feminist journalist pointing out the error of her
ways.

Damn! Gazing at Sandi's alert, breathtak-
ingly lovely face, Royke's grimace smoothed
into a gentle smile. If she weren't already
married, he'd scoop her up, take her home
with him, and barricade the door against this
propaganda-slinging reporter! What the hell
was the matter with Mike Case, anyway?
Royke asked himself for perhaps the thou-
sandth time since that editor from *Women
First* had called several weeks ago. Did Mike
require lessons on the proper care of a
woman? Gazing down at Sandi, Royke
sighed.

"So, you're really going through with it?"
he finally responded.

"Oh, Royke," Sandi scolded him. "You
knew I would."

"Yes, I knew." Royke sighed again softly.
"Still...I had hoped that you'd change your
mind."

"Oh, darling, please don't worry!" Sandi murmured urgently. "It will be all right. You'll see. I've just met her and she's a charming young woman, really."

Royke's mind had fixed on the endearment, so he barely heard Sandi's reassurance. Sandi called him darling when she wanted him on her side; it always worked. Royke adored Sandi as he would a treasured sister, and he knew, were she not deliriously happy with Mike Case, he could very easily fall in love with her. Royke sighed silently for what might have been. Sandi was the only woman he'd ever come close to loving. Frowning, Royke considered Sandi's eager expression. What had she said? Something about this reporter being charming? Oh, sure. Charming like a sidewinder!

"Is she?" Royke's tone made it clear that she had better be. Sandi obviously got his meaning loud and clear.

"Now, Royke," she half-warned, half-coaxed. "You be nice to her. You hear me?"

"I hear," Royke grunted, nodding his head sharply. "But I'm making no promises."

"I swear, you are such a bull!" Sandi's

smile softened her words. Her glance made a quick, comprehensive survey of the crowded area, then, a tiny frown drawing her brows together, she returned her gaze to his face. "Are you being met?"

"No. I'm a few days ahead of schedule, so no one is expecting me. I've arranged for a rental car." Royke frowned. "*If* my bag ever appears."

"Now, that's silly!" Sandi exclaimed. "You just cancel that car at once. You can ride home with us."

Royke's smile was a flash of white in his deeply tanned face. "I was hoping you'd say that."

It was true; he had been hoping Sandi would insist he ride home with her, but not merely to avoid the inconvenience of returning a rented car. A very strong, protective urge had risen in him. Royke wanted to be there to battle the dragon reporter if necessary.

"All ready, Sandi," announced a soft, somewhat husky voice behind him.

Royke turned and felt the breath lodge painfully in his throat. Oh, damn! Oh, hell and damnation! It couldn't be, he protested silently. But...of course, it was. A warm smile lighting her face, Sandi drew the chestnut-haired beauty around to face him.

"Stacy, I'd like you to meet our nearest neighbor and dearest friend, Royke Larson. Royke—'' Sandi's eyes flew back to him, warning dire things if he was not polite to the young woman "—Stacy Ernshaw, the reporter who will be staying with us for a while."

"Ms. Ernshaw." Taking her small, fragile-looking hand inside his much larger one, Royke groaned inwardly. Wouldn't you just know it? he thought savagely. I thought I had seen a dream and she turns out to be a nightmare. Everything inside Royke froze. Beautiful or not, he warned her silently, you had damned well better behave yourself around me, sweetheart.

As soon as she met the man's eyes, Stacy felt confused, wary, and ridiculously frightened. The first coherent thought that entered her mind was that he was even taller than he'd appeared sitting down on the plane. As she murmured a response to his dry "Ms. Ernshaw," Stacy marveled at the difference between this utterly intimidating man and the man who'd clasped her fingers so reassuringly not much more than a half hour before.

"How do you do, Mr. Larson?" Hating the trite greeting even as she uttered it, Stacy extended her hand and gazed up at him. God! He looked big and broad in the shoulders, and, at the moment, rather disapproving! Disapproving? Of her? Stacy had to work to prevent a frown from creasing her forehead. Why should the man find fault with her? He didn't even know her!

Royke Larson's grip on her hand shattered Stacy's bemusement. Good heavens! Was he trying to crush her hand? Damned if she'd allow him the satisfaction of seeing her wince, Stacy decided, suddenly unreasonably incensed.

"If you are finished with my hand?" She smiled oversweetly, lifting one delicately arched brow questioningly.

"Of course." Royke's heavier, darker brow matched her action as his fingers relaxed. Then, in what Stacy felt was a deliberate snub, he presented the back side of his shoulder to her and turned to face Sandi. "How are Mike and the kids?"

For some strange, incomprehensible reason Stacy felt more insulted than she ever had before in her life. Feeling her cheeks grow warm with embarrassment, she spun around to glare at the luggage belt, which suddenly began to move at that moment. Reminding herself that she was a mature, self-confident woman, she straightened her spine and strode toward the belt, tuning out the warm sound of Royke Larson's low voice.

Like a marauding horde, the milling, frustrated, travel-weary passengers descended on the slowly moving belt. Stacy joined the throng determinedly. Gripping the handles of her bag, she turned to fight her way through the press of bodies and careened jarringly into the unyielding mass.

"Oh! I am sorry! Please ex..." Stacy's apology died on her lips as she looked up into the narrowed eyes of Royke Larson and experienced again that strange bone-melting sensation she'd felt on the plane.

"I—I, ah..."

"Don't strain yourself, Ms. Ernshaw." Royke's drawl infuriated Stacy all over again. "If you will kindly step out of the way?" Not waiting for Stacy to comply, Royke grasped her lightly by the upper arms and moved her bodily to one side, thereby increasing her fury to pure rage.

Who did this—this *rancher* think he was anyway? Ignoring the heat singeing her flesh where his hands had gripped her, she attempted to glare holes into his broad back. Boorish provincial! Stacy flung the insult at Royke silently, then feeling both foolish and childish, she made her way through the crowd to where Sandi waited patiently.

"You look a trifle harassed," Sandi said sympathetically when Stacy broke free of the crowd. "Did someone give you the elbow in there?"

"No." Stacy smiled weakly, thinking, no, not the elbow, the sharp side of the tongue! "I'm just beginning to feel a little drained from the flight, I guess." Stacy's smile grew stronger. "I'm really a white-knuckle flier, you know."

"You're kidding!" Sandi laughed. "So am

I! I need at least three double bourbons before boarding a plane for even the shortest flight!''

They were laughing together like old school chums when Royke's voice sliced through their hilarity, bringing a flash to Stacy's dark blue eyes, and a gleam to Sandi's smoky-gray ones.

''Isn't the baggage-claim area of an airport a rather strange place to have a party?''

''Oh, Royke,'' Sandi admonished him gently, still grinning. ''You are absolutely no fun at all when you're tired.'' Linking her arm through Stacy's, she murmured conspiratorially, ''I think we'd better take this grouchy old devil home. Don't you?''

Stacy felt her smile slip into a frown. This was the first inkling she'd had that the tall rancher would be riding with them, and the knowledge made mincemeat of her good humor. Why didn't he simply fade into the sunset like all right-thinking cowboys were supposed to do? she thought irritably. Then her thoughts were scattered as Royke impatiently relieved her of her suitcase.

''I am perfectly capable of carrying my

own bag!'' she snapped, nonetheless relinquishing the valise when he tugged on it.

"I'm sure you are," he drawled lazily. "And maybe in Philadelphia a man would let you. But you're not in Philadelphia now, are you? And out here the men still do the carrying—at least whenever possible."

Before Stacy could come up with a retort, she found herself being politely, if firmly, hustled out of the terminal building and through the parking area.

When they finally came to a stop at the car, a dusty, battered station wagon, Royke preemptively plucked the car keys from Sandi's slim fingers.

"If you don't mind, sweetheart, I'll drive." Royke's tone clearly indicated that he couldn't care less if "sweetheart" minded or not. "The way you two were convulsed with the giggles back there, I'll feel a lot safer behind the wheel than riding shotgun." Though he lifted one dark brow at Sandi, it was obvious the matter was settled; Sandi merely nodded meekly and smiled beguilingly.

Stacy, on the other hand, felt fit to be tied, and for more than one reason. Not only had she been consigned to the back seat, but her hostess had revealed a simpering acquiescence to Royke's blatant chauvinism! Swallowing a stinging remark, Stacy crawled into the car with as much dignity as she could muster, promising herself she'd personally see to Sandi's equal-rights education before she returned to civilization.

Sliding along the cracked plastic seat, Stacy positioned herself directly behind Royke. That way Sandi could converse with both of them by sitting sideways on the front seat.

Sandi glanced back at Stacy and smiled. "You'll have to forgive the condition of the wreck," she said, indicating the shabby upholstering. "The car gets used pretty hard, by a passel of people. As soon as we can scrape the money together, we plan to retire this heap. Till then..." Her voice trailed away and she shrugged in a totally unconcerned way. "We had hoped to be able to replace it this year, but the engine in the four-wheel drive gave up the ghost...." Again her voice faded and she slid her smiling glance to Royke. "As Grouchy here can verify, the four-wheel drive is of paramount importance on a working ranch.''

Slicing a glance at the rearview mirror, Royke stared with piercing directness into Stacy's eyes, giving her the uncomfortable sensation of being pinned to the seat. ''The four-wheel drive is of paramount importance on a working ranch,'' he parroted, releasing his visual hold on Stacy by shifting his eyes back to the road.

Having the sensation of being dismissed, Stacy squirmed inwardly and glared at the back of his head. Why, she wondered, had he suddenly taken so intense a dislike to her? Especially after he'd been so very understanding on the plane. From the very moment Sandi had introduced her to him, Royke had seemed to exude rejection. Stacy knew it couldn't have been anything she'd said, for she'd uttered nothing but the most mundane responses to his less than enthusiastic greeting. Perhaps the man was always erratic, swinging alternately from pleasant to nasty without reason.

At that moment Sandi drew Stacy's attention.

"So, what do you think of the place?" she asked lightly.

Blinking, Stacy came to the realization that she'd been staring out the side window without seeing a thing. "It's—it's beautiful country," she blurted out, scanning the terrain swiftly. From her quick glance Stacy saw that they were traveling through a wide valley that appeared to be completely surrounded by mountains, whose peaks looked dark blue in the waning afternoon sunlight.

Turning from the window to speak to Sandi, Stacy's gaze became entangled with the mocking brown eyes reflected in the rearview mirror. He knows damn well I haven't been admiring the landscape! Stacy thought, dragging her gaze from his.

"Do we have much farther to go?" she asked Sandi with forced calm. At that moment she actually hated Royke Larson for having the power to rattle her.

"We're on R-L land now." Sandi smiled, indicating their taciturn driver. "Our spread lies to the east of Royke's." Laughing easily, she settled herself more comfortably into her seat. "Actually," she continued, "compared to Royke's outfit, our holding could more accurately be called a plot!''

"You're surviving," Royke inserted flatly.

"Just!" Sandi retorted, not unpleasantly. Switching her attention back to Stacy, she added, "And we wouldn't even be eating regularly if it weren't for ol' Grouchy here.''

"Bury it, Sandi." Royke's tone held a hint of command. "Mike's a good cattleman. He'd survive without my assistance, and you know it.''

Sandi's features softened at the mention of her husband. Stacy couldn't miss catching the glow in the other woman's eyes. Something urged her to check the mirror again. The sight that met her eyes had Stacy wishing she'd denied the urge. Though the glance Royke sent over Sandi's face was brief, what he saw obviously dismayed him.

He's in love with her! The notion created a clenching sensation in Stacy's middle not unlike what she'd felt on the plane. Lowering her lashes, she shifted her gaze from Royke to Sandi and back again. Was there a little extramarital hanky-panky going on here? Sandi was now smiling softly at Royke, and

Royke had relaxed considerably. Still, Stacy mused, it was hard to tell if there was anything of a romantic nature between them.

Why the devil should you care anyway? she chided herself, swallowing the sudden bitter taste in her mouth. For heaven's sake, practically every one of your friends is either having an affair or just finished with one— and every one of your friends is married! Why should it upset you if two virtual strangers are indulging their physical appetites? Why should you care?

Stacy could find no answer. All she knew was that she did care very much—too much for her own peace of mind. Avoiding the whole issue, she brought her attention back to the soft conversation going on in the front seat.

"...and that only gives you a slight edge," Royke was insisting.

"Not so slight," Sandi disputed him. What they were talking about, Stacy hadn't a clue. As Sandi went on, tilting her head at Stacy to let her know she was included in on the ongoing argument, the conversation became more understandable. "You know better than

I that keeping a running inventory of our beef on your computer has helped us immeasurably.''

Stacy frowned as Royke shrugged. Ranchers were into computers now? How had she missed that bit of information while doing her research?

"We're home, Stacy."

Jerked out of her bemusement, Stacy smiled apologetically at her hostess. "I'm sorry, I wasn't paying attention. I was digesting the information that ranchers are into computers." As Sandi explained, Stacy looked around at her home. Fortunately, Stacy had resisted the impulse to form a mental picture of the Case homestead. Now, glancing around, she was glad she had, for never would she have imagined the weathered, boxlike building that met her surprised eyes.

"You don't have to scour your mind for an inoffensive opinion, Stacy." Sandi laughed, unashamed of her home. "Actually, the back looks a lot better than the front." Linking her arm through Stacy's, she started toward the house, explaining, "Mike is re-

modeling slowly, from the back to the front.''
Her smile flashed. ''It's all my fault. I fairly
begged for a modern kitchen.''

As evening was fast overtaking the day-
light, the air had grown decidedly cold and
Stacy didn't have to be urged into the warmth
of the house. And warmth was exactly what
she found. If, Stacy decided mere seconds after entering, the outside of the house was run-
down and uninviting, the inside was all bright
colors and brighter faces.

One man, three children, and two dogs con-
verged on them as they stepped over the
threshold, each one displaying varying de-
grees of boisterousness. The man, whom
Stacy correctly assumed was Mike Case, was
the most restrained of the welcoming party.

Almost as tall as Royke, Mike was much
thinner, almost gangly, and very attractive in
a fresh-scrubbed way. In the brightly lit living
room, Stacy could see that Mike's eyes were
a changeable hazel color. A gentle smile lit
his face as he gazed at his wife, his expression one of near adoration. Stacy liked him at
once.

The children, a boy of about seven, a girl

of possibly five, and another boy no more than three, were a beautiful composite of Sandi and Mike. And, at that moment, they were extremely noisy. Flinging themselves at their mother, they hung on to her like little limpets while she made the introductions.

"Now, hear this!" Sandi shouted. "What will Ms. Ernshaw think of you three heathens?" Completely ruining her attempt at sternness by hugging the three to her hips, Sandi went on quietly. "Stacy, this assortment of humanity at its loudest is my one pure pride and joy." Beaming at Stacy, she indicated the patiently waiting man. "My husband, Mike."

"Ms. Ernshaw," Mike said softly, extending his large, bony hand.

"Stacy, please." As she placed her hand in Mike's, Stacy was amazed at the ripple of emotion that fluttered in her chest. She felt an unfamiliar flash of envy for Sandi. Envy? For a woman who lived in a box at the back door to nowhere?

Stacy was given no time to examine her feelings, for Sandi was ruffling the curly brown hair of her firstborn and saying, "And this is Mike Jr. Mike, say 'Pleased to meet you' to the young lady.''

Wide brown eyes stared up at Stacy a moment, then Mike Jr. grinned and won Stacy's heart.

"I'm pleased to meet you, Miss Ernshaw." Young Mike thrust out his hand in imitation of his father.

"And I'm very pleased to meet you, Mike," Stacy assured him solemnly, gripping his hand firmly.

"And this is Laura," Sandi said, smiling down at the five-year-old. "Our destroyer of men's hearts."

Shifting her gaze to the doe-eyed little beauty, Stacy believed that some fine day Laura would indeed be capable of breaking hearts.

Laura whispered, "Hello," giggled, then hid her face against her mother's thigh.

Stacy earned herself another giggle by bending down to whisper back, "Hello, darling."

"And finally," Sandi said dramatically, "this bundle of energy is David Royke, named for his godfather, Royke David." Releasing the other two children, she scooped the toddler into her arms. "Will you say hello to Miss Ernshaw, love?"

The boy hugged his mother. Then, glancing over her shoulder, he smiled in delight and threw his arms out wide.

"Uncle Royke!"

"Hi-ya, slugger." Royke's low, drawling voice, coming from so close behind Stacy, sent a tingle down her spine. Stiffening against the bewildering effect his nearness had on her nerves, she concentrated on keeping her smile intact. It wasn't easy, and Royke made it harder still when he spoke again, for he had drawn even closer to her, so close in fact that Stacy could actually feel the warmth of his body.

"Do you think we could move into the room?" he suggested lazily. "I'm beginning to feel slightly crowded in this six inches of floor space between the door and Ms. Ernshaw."

Chapter Three

An instant of silence greeted Royke's request, then Sandi laughed.

"Of course!" Shooing the children and dogs before her, Sandi led the way into the living room, issuing orders as she went. "Mike, would you please take Stacy's suitcase? Mikey, you're in charge of hanging up Ms. Ernshaw's and Uncle Royke's coats. Laura, will you *please* clear your dolls and dollhouse off the sofa?" Turning abruptly, she thrust David into Royke's arms. "And you," she directed, "can have the dubious pleasure of controlling this wiggle worm for a few minutes." The humans taken care of, Sandi planted her hands on her hips and glowered down at the excited canines. "And who let these animals into *my* living room?" she demanded.

Stacy observed the domestic chaos in a state of amusement. Never in all her twenty-five years had she been part of a family scene such as this. Stacy knew her mother would have been appalled. As a matter of fact, she felt quite positive that every one of her friends would be similarly shocked, merely because neither her mother nor her friends ever spent enough time with their children to experience this type of pandemonium. People who were *involved* simply did not have the *time!*

"Come with me, Stacy. I'll show you to your room. By the time you've freshened up a bit, I'll have a drink ready for you." Stacy heard the underlying amusement in her tone. "I imagine by now you could use a stiff one."

As she went through the house, Stacy found herself revising her earlier opinion of it. The interior was much larger than she would have guessed. As she followed Sandi it became obvious that the building was constructed in an L-shaped design. What she'd been able to see from the front had been the bottom stroke of the L.

At the far end of the living room they entered a long hall through an archway. Stacy realized at once that this part of the building was the long stroke of the L, and not part of the original structure.

"I'm afraid you'll have to share the bathroom with the kids," Sandi informed her not at all apologetically as they walked along the hall. "The only private bathroom is connected to the master bedroom, and inaccessible from the hall." She indicated the bathroom as they passed it. The door was ajar and Stacy caught a quick glimpse of a clean, plastic-tiled, functional bathroom.

They had already passed the doors to four rooms, and Sandi strode by yet another before she came to a stop at the last one at the end of the hall.

"It's nothing fancy," she warned, swinging the door open and preceding Stacy inside. "The room is used mainly for storage." She tossed a grin over her shoulder. "I did clean the junk out of here, though."

The room, though small, was spotless and completely clear of any sign of junk. The furnishings consisted of a narrow daybed, an old but well-cared-for chest of drawers, a straight-back chair, and a small table upon which rested a welcoming pot of forced daffodils.

After making a circuit of the room, Stacy's glance returned to Sandi. "For a storage room," she commented dryly, "it makes a very comfortable guest room."

"Sure, that's easy for you to say...now." Sandi laughed. "But you may change your mind by tomorrow morning, after you've spent a night on that poor excuse for a bed." Stepping into the hall, she called back, "Don't worry about unpacking now. I'll help you with it after dinner. What would you like to drink?"

"White wine?"

"You got it," Sandi called back from halfway down the hall.

A smile curving the corners of her mouth, Stacy dropped her shoulder bag on the bed and shrugged out of her suit jacket. Then, after rolling the long sleeves of her chocolate brown blouse to her elbows, she dug her makeup case from her bag and headed for the bathroom.

Some ten minutes later, while applying a light coat of moisturizer to her freshly scrubbed face, Stacy examined her features in the medicine cabinet mirror above the sink. What was it about the arrangement of those features that caused such a strong antipathy in Royke?

Stacy frowned. Her skin was soft and clear, her complexion creamy. Her jawline was well-defined, if a trifle square, her nose was not too short, not too long, and neatly slim. Her brow was wide and smooth, and her eyes…Stacy was well aware of the fact that her eyes were her best feature. Of a deep, dark blue, her eyes were the first thing most people noticed about her. Set wide apart, they were fringed by naturally long, dark brown lashes. All together, her features combined to present a rather appealing picture. If not ravishingly beautiful, at least she was pleasingly attractive. So then, what was it about her that had turned Royke Larson off?

Was she too small, too slender, her hair too curly? Stacy sighed as she replaced the mocha-shaded eye shadow applicator in the tortoiseshell case. Why should she even care what the tall rancher thought of her? She would be with the Cases for only a few days at most, and she would very likely never see Royke again. Who gave a damn what he thought, anyway?

You do.

Stacy stared solemnly into the depths of the honest eyes gazing back at her. What her own mind had told her was true. She did care what Royke thought of her. Now the question was: Why should she care? The man was a complete stranger, and would probably remain one.

Unwilling to delve too deeply into her unusual reaction to the man, Stacy swung out of the bathroom and across the hall to her room. Be polite to him, she advised herself, be pleasant, but, at all costs, do not allow yourself to get too close!

Tossing the makeup case on the dresser,

Stacy picked up her jacket, then, feeling quite warm enough without it, dropped it onto the bed again. After pausing at the mirror attached to the dresser to adjust her silk blouse, button the cuffs of her sleeves, and rake a brush through her defiantly springy curls, she left the room more than ready for a cool glass of wine.

Her composure intact, Stacy allowed a small smile to play over her lips as she neared the archway to the living room. The sounds of muted conversation and soft laughter came from inside and Stacy felt all the tension of the day drain out of her.

Yet as she hesitated, framed in the archway, a new feeling of nervousness gripped her small figure. This time it was not caused by her fear of flying or the pain in her stomach, or even by the baffling anger she'd felt since she was introduced to Royke at the airport. This particular type of tension was strictly sexual, and the reason for it stood across the room from her.

Royke looked so damned good, it was positively demoralizing! As yet unnoticed, Stacy stood, her heartbeat increasing by quantum leaps, her breathing decreasing to shallow gasps, staring at the tall man standing in front of the natural-stone fireplace.

Royke had removed his very conservative, charcoal gray suit jacket and, clad in slacks, a vest, and a pristine white shirt, he looked casually elegant, wholly masculine, and sexy as hell! His stance was indolent, almost lazy, with one arm resting lightly on the mantelpiece, the other bending at the elbow as he raised a drink to his smiling lips. His eyes were softened by warmth and affection, and fastened on Sandi's face.

In a blinding instant of self-perception, Stacy knew that she would happily surrender anything, everything that she possessed to have him gaze upon her like that.

Shaken by the intensity of her emotions, Stacy dragged her gaze from Royke's harshly etched, craggy visage. A physical reaction, nothing more, she assured herself. A long-overdue chemical explosion inside her body. Everything female in her responding to everything male in him. Nothing more. God, Stacy prayed it was nothing more!

* * *

Without knowing quite how he knew, Royke knew the instant Stacy came to a halt in the archway. With a barely perceptible flicker of his eyes he ran a quick but thorough glance over her small form, and felt all the moisture in his mouth and throat dry up.

Everything about her appealed to him—everything. The fingers that clung to the glass in his hand itched to dive into the unruly mass of curls that covered her head and framed her lovely face. His dry lips ached to drink the moisture from her invitingly glossy mouth. His body trembled with the need to impress itself on the softness of hers. And, Lord! At that instant he wanted nothing so much as he wanted to merge his flesh with hers, claiming her so all the world would know that she belonged to him.

Royke didn't particularly like the possessiveness inherent in his desire, but there was not a damn thing he could do about it. He wanted Stacy badly, more than he'd ever wanted any other woman. Hell, he didn't even know her, he thought, lifting the glass to gulp thirstily at his whiskey. Know her or not, like her or not, he wanted her!

Made wary by these realizations, Royke advised himself to get busy erecting a few barriers between them.

Still poised in the archway, Stacy reaffirmed her determination to keep her distance from Royke Larson. In some way, possibly in every way, this man could harm her. Subconsciously, Stacy knew that unless she was very careful, she'd be running the risk of leaving Montana a vastly different person than she had been before she arrived.

Determined to return home exactly the same as when she'd left, Stacy straightened her spine and strolled into the room, grateful for the whim that had made her pause in the archway. The interlude had lasted mere seconds but in those few seconds she had made a momentous discovery.

Concealing her sudden anxiety behind a facade of composure, Stacy sauntered to the couch and sat down beside Sandi.

"Oh, there you are!" Sandi smiled warmly. "And there is your wine." She nodded at the delicately fluted glass on the coffee table. "Dinner will be ready in a few

minutes." Sandi arched her brows quizzically. "I imagine you must be starved by
now."

"I think *famished* comes closer to the
mark," Stacy admitted. She never could eat
on airplanes, and had consumed only a hasty
breakfast of juice and toast and the small container of milk she'd bought during the layover
in Chicago. Even as she swallowed some of
the dry white wine, Stacy knew that drinking
alcohol at this time was not too bright. It was
now over twelve hours since she'd eaten her
meager breakfast, and a tiny carton of milk
could hardly be called an adequate lunch. Be
careful, she cautioned herself, or you'll be
smashed before you get to the dinner table.

Taking another, much smaller sip, Stacy
sent a frowning glance around the room.
"Where are the children? And the small
horses?"

"The kids are in the boys' bedroom watching TV," Sandi said. "The small horses have
been returned to their kennels at the rear of
the house. And, as that lovely man there—"
with a wave of her hand she indicated Mike,
sprawled lazily in a fireside chair opposite

them "—fed the kids before we got home, we'll be able to have our meal in peace."

"You failed to mention that this lovely man prepared the meal, as well," Mike chided in a tone that matched his posture.

"Best damn little housewife in the state," Royke inserted dryly.

Though Stacy felt a tremor of annoyance at Royke's taunt, Mike and Sandi merely grinned at each other. Didn't the man have a home? she wondered irritably. Wasn't there someone waiting for him, expecting him? That thought sent a chill crawling down Stacy's spine. *Was* there someone waiting for Royke? Some female someone? Startled by the feeling of sickness that washed over her, Stacy forced her attention back to the banter being tossed between Mike and Royke.

"...Yes, well, you're secretly ticked off because you can't whip a decent casserole together," Mike retorted, obviously used to the other man's taunts.

"Who the hell likes casseroles?" Royke drawled.

"Royke Larson!" Sandi exclaimed, launching herself into the fray. "*You're* the

one who always makes a pig of himself with
my casseroles!''

"That's correct," Royke conceded. "But I
make a real hog of myself over your roast
beef." He then had the gall to smile smugly.
"Mike's roast beef is barely fit to use for
slopping the hogs." He smiled at Sandi, the
same kind of tender smile that Stacy had witnessed when she'd paused before entering the
room. Once again she felt oddly hurt. "Personally," Royke drawled on, "I'd just as
soon Mike stuck to what he does best—
ranching." Though Stacy wouldn't have believed it possible, Royke's smile softened
even more. "Being the old-fashioned sort, I
prefer a woman's touch in the kitchen."

Quickly gulping at her wine, Stacy managed to swallow the exclamation of angry
protest that rose in her throat. The absolute
gall of the man! By his own admission Royke
had labeled himself a pig. Silently Stacy went
him one further—in her opinion Royke was
an old-fashioned male chauvinist pig! A
woman's touch in the kitchen, indeed! Adding fuel to her anger was the realization that
Royke was obviously staying for dinner.

Was the man totally devoid of sensitivity? Stacy wondered. Why didn't he just go home and give her and Sandi a chance to get to know each other?

He's protecting her! The answer flashed into Stacy's mind, and with it a surge of anger. Anger and something else, some strange new emotion that Stacy refused to contemplate...at least not here, and not now.

Raising her eyes to glare at him over the rim of her glass, Stacy nearly choked on a sip of wine as her gaze collided with his. Once again Stacy had the uncomfortable sensation of being pinned to her seat. Mockery shimmered in the depths of his dark eyes and danced at the corners of his thin lips. He was baiting her! Stacy could read it as clearly as a first-grade primer. But why? What was Royke Larson's problem? She had no time to ponder that question, for Royke was making yet another outrageous remark.

"...And the next thing I'll hear is that you've joined some militant group and are marching for, or against, something or other."

Sandi's delighted laughter effectively cov-

ered Stacy's indignant gasp. She *had* marched
on occasion—both for and against!

Though Stacy longed to improve Royke's
education, she was relieved when Sandi
voiced her opinion and saved Stacy the discomfort of being cast in the role of argumen-
tative guest.

"But, Royke, if I feel strongly about an
issue, why shouldn't I say so loud and
clear?" Sandi inquired sweetly. "Oh, I don't
mean by actually marching, or sitting in, or
anything like that," she went on earnestly.
"But by aligning myself with others who feel
as I do."

"You'd align yourself with the man-
haters?" Royke asked astringently.

"Man-haters!" Sandi laughed.

Man-haters? Stacy repeated silently. Was
that his problem? she thought with a fresh
burst of anger. Mr. Royke "Chauvinist" Larson is afraid I'm going to corrupt the happy
homemaker! Oh, horrors, wherever will he go
for his roast beef dinner if Sandi is led astray
by the big bad feminist?

Again, lost in her outrage, Stacy had
missed whatever response Royke had made,

and now it was Mike's voice that drew her attention.

"Ah, I was wondering," he inserted dryly, "if you two would mind shelving your discussion—and I use the term very lightly—till after dinner." As three pairs of eyes settled on him, Mike grinned, not unlike his endearing youngest son. "I'd really like to sit down to the meal *I* prepared while it's still fit to eat."

Stacy thought she could actually see the tension drain out of Royke as he grinned lazily back at Mike. With that grin all the energy seemed to drain out of Stacy. God! The effect he had on her senses was devastating!

"Lead on, host of mine," Royke urged Mike, his grin widening into a flashing white smile. "I'll escort your guest to the table." Straightening away from the mantel, Royke crooked an elbow, offering it to Stacy in a broad parody of courtly manners. "Ms. Ernshaw. May I have the—" there was a tiny pause that only Stacy noticed "—pleasure?"

Shock held Stacy motionless for an instant, but not shock at Royke's disdainful behavior. No, the shock freezing Stacy was caused by

the strength of the anger rioting through her.
For the first time in her life Stacy was filled
with the need to strike another person! In fact,
before she became conscious of it, her fingers
curled into a fist. The only thing that pre-
vented that fist from hurtling toward his smiling face was the control she immediately im-
posed upon herself.

That Royke was fully aware of the fight
raging inside her, and the reason for it, was
evidenced by the dark brow he arched at her
in mockery.

"Careful," he warned her in a tone pitched
low enough to reach Stacy's ears but not
those of Sandi and Mike, who had started to
stroll out of the room. "You may have come
a long way, baby, but not *that* long a way."
When Stacy ignored the arm he'd offered her
he let it drop and grasped her hand, prying
her fingers open with his. "And not nearly
long enough to try a roundhouse right on
me."

The hard, callused palm that met hers
seemed to ignite sparks in Stacy's hand.
Never had she felt anything like the heat that
radiated from her palm to her arm and up into

her shoulder. Then, incredibly, her entire side grew warm. Royke was too near, much too near, and Stacy was suddenly much too aware of him both physically and mentally. Glancing quickly at the archway to assure herself that Sandi and Mike had left the room, Stacy tugged sharply against Royke's hold, gasping in protest when he anchored her to his side by lacing his fingers through hers.

"I thought I'd come far enough to outdistance *your* type," Stacy said in a furious whisper, stiffening her fingers against his grip. "And don't call me baby!"

Royke made a noise that sounded very much like a snort. "If there were more men of my *type*," he whispered back, "there would be a helluva lot less broads of *your* type...*sweetheart*."

"My type! *My* type!" Stacy sputtered. "What do you mean by my type? And don't call me sweetheart, either!"

"You know damn well what I mean," Royke muttered. "And how do you propose to stop me from calling you baby, or sweetheart, or anything else?" All the while he was taunting her, he was tugging her along toward the archway.

Digging in her heels, Stacy managed to halt his progress. "I do not know what you mean! And will you stop pulling at me?"

Royke went still for an instant, then, drawing a deep breath, he loosened his hold on her fingers. "Look, we're both guests in this house," he said calmly. "Sandi and Mike are waiting to share a meal with us. Do you think you could possibly disguise your dislike for me for the length of that meal?"

Stacy glared at him. How dare he! After the looks and barely veiled insults he'd thrown at her. How dare he blame her! Actually trembling with rage, Stacy opened her mouth to berate him, only to close it again with a snap when the corners of his lips curved into a smile of satisfaction.

He wants me to scream at him like some harridan! The realization that she was being manipulated turned her anger to icy calm. Her eyes narrowing, she smiled back at him. Two can play at this game, cowboy.

"Thattagirl," he crooned insultingly. "Bank the militant fire." Tugging on her hand, he again started for the other room. As they approached the archway, he let fly a final taunt. ''And I'd advise you to keep that fire banked throughout your entire visit.''

With that, they stepped into the kitchen. To Stacy's amazement, Royke's demeanor changed completely. In a flash all sign of her antagonist was gone. In his stead was a smiling, utterly charming man. Dumbfounded, Stacy mutely followed as he guided her to the table in the beautifully remodeled room.

''You two getting to know each other?'' Smiling contentedly, Sandi glanced at them as they drew to a stop at the butcher-block table she was busily setting.

''Yes.'' Royke bestowed a gentle smile on Sandi. ''And I'm finding the process quite interesting.'' Angling his head, he gazed down at Stacy, his smile fading. ''What about you, *Stacy?*'' One dark eyebrow shot up in challenge as he emphasized her name.

''Very interesting,'' Stacy concurred pleasantly, her eyes accepting his challenge. ''Mr.—'' her smile held contempt only he could see ''—ah...*Royke* is a very interesting study.''

Ignoring the flame that leapt into his eyes, Stacy moved casually away from his unnerving proximity. ''Is there something I can do to help?'' she asked Sandi quietly.

''Not a thing,'' Sandi replied blithely, obviously unaware of the tension shimmering between her guests. ''Mike's washing up. Everything's ready, so we can sit down to eat as soon as he's finished.''

''He's finished.'' Mike's easy drawl preceded him into the kitchen. ''And starving. Let's dish it up, honey.''

Honey. Sweetheart. Baby! Were all Western men sexists? Stacy wondered, seating herself in the cane-back chair Sandi indicated with a wave of her hand. Oh, and let us not forget ''girl,'' she added to herself, hearing again Royke's condescending ''Thattagirl.'' Lord, it had been years since she'd been addressed as *girl*, let alone sweetheart or baby!

Stacy recalled Royke's sarcastic tone as he'd flung the endearments at her in a way that made them sound like dirty words. With the deep attractiveness of Royke's voice, what would it sound like if he'd said those same words honestly?

For an instant Stacy's fork paused in midair between her plate and her mouth. In that instant she could hear the rough velvet sound of his voice murmuring love words to her, and a shiver of response went skipping along her spine.

Stacy Anne Ernshaw! Are you absolutely mad? Stacy demanded of herself as she forced her hand into motion. The very last thing you need, or want, is the attention of a man— especially this kind of man!

Chewing her food automatically, Stacy gazed up at Royke from under her lashes and immediately wished she had not.

Royke was staring at her with naked desire blazing out of his eyes.

Chapter Four

You, friend, are totally out of your mind.

Royke issued the declaration mutely as he urged the Cases' station wagon up the curving road to his home. Although the much-used wagon complained every inch of the way, it completed the trip, coughing with a final shudder as Royke brought it to a stop a few feet in front of the double garage that was set to the right rear of the natural-stone-and-glass ranch house.

Home. Previously Royke had always felt a leap of pleasure at the sight of his domain.

Tonight all Royke felt was an unfamiliar emptiness and a gnawing hunger.

Standing motionless by the car in the biting cold, Royke raised his head to gaze at the bright moon and starlit sky. With sharp insight he realized that what he'd felt for Sandi had been a twinge in comparison to the all-encompassing ache he was feeling now for Stacy Ernshaw.

"Damn!"

Muttering the word aloud, Royke pushed himself away from the wagon and strolled slowly to the back door of the modern split-level house, his glance noting the light that sprang to life in a room slightly above the kitchen.

Not a damn thing happens around here without Cassie's knowledge, he thought wryly. Even at seventy-two the woman who'd been housekeeper for the Larsons since before Royke's birth didn't miss a single trick. The door swung open as he inserted his key.

"Royke Larson!" Cassie Flannagan began scolding him before Royke had a foot through the doorway. "Why didn't you let a body know you were coming?"

"What body was that, Cassie love?" Royke teased her, bending to kiss the tiny woman's parchmentlike cheek. "Anyone interesting?"

"Go on with you!" Drawing back enough to cast a critical look over his tall form, Cassie frowned. "You look tired. When did you leave Calgary?"

"Early this morning." Royke grimaced as he walked to the double-size refrigerator. "Very early this morning."

Cassie's mouth and eyes opened wide. "It took you from early this morning till after eleven o'clock at night to get from Calgary to Montana?" She gasped in astonishment.

"No, Cass." Shaking his head, Royke opened the refrigerator door and withdrew a can of beer. He popped the tab and took a large swallow before continuing. "The plane landed late this afternoon. I ran into Sandi Case at the airport and she insisted I ride home with them." After another deep swallow of beer, Royke grinned. "She also insisted I stay for dinner. Dinner conversation carried over to after-dinner coffee and liqueur." He shrugged. "You know how it is."

Not for an instant did Royke think it odd that he, the ranch owner, was explaining his movements to his housekeeper. To Royke, Cassie was the grandmother he'd never known, and the mother he'd lost to another man when he was not yet ten years old.

"Them?" Quick-witted as ever, Cassie had latched on to that one word.

Royke frowned in confusion. "What?"

Raising her eyes to the ceiling, Cassie shook her head impatiently. "You said Sandi invited you to ride home with *them*. Was the whole Case outfit with her, then?"

"No, of course not." Sliding a chair away from the long table that ran down the center of the big room, Royke dropped tiredly into it, stretching his long legs out in front of him. "Sandi drove to the airport alone to meet someone." He emptied the can in a gulp. "That reporter arrived from Philadelphia today."

"And so, what did you think of her?" Without being asked, Cassie went to the fridge to get him another beer.

Royke's eyes narrowed as his fingers crushed the can in his hand. Big deal, he thought, the damn thing's made of aluminum, any eight-year-old could crush it as easily.

"Have you fallen asleep with your eyes open?" Cassie asked sharply.

"No, light of my life. I have not fallen asleep...yet." Stretching muscles tight with the previous hours' tension, Royke sliced a glance at Cassie. "What was the question?"

"The reporter. The one from Philadelphia," Cassie said succinctly. "What is she like?"

Like everything I expected...and like no one I've ever met before. Swallowing back a sigh with a fresh swig of beer, Royke studied the tips of his seldom worn, handmade, Italian leather dress shoes. "She's younger than I expected," he finally responded. "And very attractive...no, she's not attractive." He smiled in self-mockery. "Ms. Stacy Ernshaw is a beautiful woman." Royke missed the speculative gleam in Cassie's eyes.

"I...see," she said softly, revealingly.

Royke did not miss the note of hope in Cassie's tone. Lifting his gaze, he met her stare directly, an ironic smile tilting the corners of his lips.

"No, Cassie, you don't see anything. I said she is beautiful—outside." Unaware that the sigh he gave was more telling than mere words, he went on in a flat tone. "The impression she gives on first sight is of delicate beauty and soft femininity with a hint of vulnerability." His smile twisted. "The immediate response...*male* response is to protect her." He gave a low, not-very-pleasant chuckle. "Ms. Ernshaw needs about as much protection as a cornered rattler. Her facade is all sugar and spice, but inside she's one tough cookie."

"Royke."

Disregarding the note of concern in Cassie's voice, Royke carefully placed his beer can on the table and stood up, yawning widely as he stretched his arms.

"I'm beat." Bending swiftly, he brushed his lips over Cassie's cheek. "I'm going to bed for a week." A spark of genuine humor lit his eyes for a moment. "Or at least till six tomorrow morning. Good night, Cass." With a final, gentle smile he strode out of the kitchen.

"Good night," Cassie responded automat-

ically, a frown adding another line to her forehead. Then, remembering, she called after
him, "And welcome home, Royke."

"Yeah, sure...thanks." His voice drifted
back to her from the short flight of steps at
the other side of the house, the side that
housed his bedroom and office/den.

Worry scoring her face, Cassie stood staring at the now-empty doorway, her eyes shad-
owed with concern. This tall man, whom she
still thought of as her baby, was hurting...and
Cassie was hurting with him.

Suddenly feeling the weight of every one
of her seventy-two years, Cassie lowered herself into the chair Royke had so recently va-
cated. Dropping her eyes to the immaculate
tabletop, Cassie gazed into the past—Royke's
past.

From the moment he'd drawn his first
breath, Royke had been the child of Cassie's
heart if not of her body. At the time of
Royke's birth Cassie Flanagan had already
been with the Larsons for twenty years, having come to the family directly from Ireland
at the age of eighteen as a nursemaid employed by Royke's grandmother. At that time

Royke's father had been a handsome but rambunctious ten-year-old—too much for his already ailing mother to handle. At Jenny Larson's death nine years later, Cassie had long since taken over the role of housekeeper for Royke's grandfather, Brendon Larson.

Thrown from a horse five years later, Brendon followed the wife he'd never ceased grieving for, leaving his only child, Brendon Junior, heir to his vast holdings at the age of twenty-four. Alone, and lonely for companionship, young Brendon had spent long periods of time away from the ranch, leaving the house in the capable hands of Cassie, and the land in the equally capable hands of his ranch foreman, Matt Parker. Matt Parker, at sixty-eight, was still foreman and still very capable.

When young Brendon finally came home to stay, he brought with him a bride, a stunningly beautiful Boston debutante. Clarissa Larson—née Bellmont—was willful, spoiled and hated the isolation of the ranch from the first week of her tenancy. And so it was that at the birth of her first and only child, Clarissa turned her face away and the attending phy-

sician placed the lustily squalling infant into
the eager arms of Cassie Flannagan. Cassie
had held Royke in her heart every day of her
life since then.

And now Cassie's baby was hurting, and
Cassie was hurting, too. Cassie felt a dull
ache in her chest as she relived Royke's
growing-up years. Both she and Matt Parker
had done everything they could think of to
alleviate the painful confusion young Royke
suffered at the hands of his disinterested
mother. Though Clarissa had never actually
abused the child in a physical sense, she had
inflicted a much deeper cruelty by denying
the boy her love. And, though his father obviously loved him, Brendon was so consumed
with his own hurt and confusion, there was
nothing left of him to give to his son. Brendon was madly in love with Clarissa, which
made it unanimous, for Clarissa was also
madly in love with Clarissa.

Although it destroyed Brendon when Clarissa, swathed in furs, her mountain of baggage preceding her, sailed out of the ranch
house never to return, Cassie had breathed a
heartfelt sigh of relief. Finally, she had

thought, tears welling in her eyes as she'd stared at the anguish on the ten-year-old Royke's face, finally Brendon would notice his son.

Sadly, things had not turned out the way Cassie had thought they would. Brendon closed himself off from all personal contact by withdrawing into work. Before her eyes Cassie saw the warm, gentle Brendon turn into a cold, ruthless money-grubber.

When Brendon died from the effects of a series of massive strokes the year Royke reached his majority, he bequeathed to his son a legacy of great material wealth in land, oil wells, and shares in several copper mines. Only Cassie and Matt Parker were left to see the other legacy of abject emotional poverty.

Shaking herself out of her reverie, Cassie brushed at her damp face with wrinkled, trembling fingers and got slowly to her feet. Sighing softly, she gathered up the empty beer cans to deposit them into the trash can under the sink. Walking slowly out of the kitchen, she paused to gaze at the short flight of stairs that led to Royke's private quarters. Once again she saw the vulnerable expression in his dark eyes that contradicted the twist of cynicism on his thin lips.

Cassie more than anyone else was fully aware that along with his tall, strong frame and masculine good looks Royke had inherited his forebears' capacity for deep, abiding love. She was also fully aware that Royke guarded his heart with more vigilance than he guarded his material inheritance.

For some time now Cassie had worried that Royke had given his heart to Sandi Case and, in doing so, had damned himself to the same barren, unsatisfying existence his father had endured. She knew that not even under the threat of death would Royke poach on another's preserves. Now Cassie had a new worry.

What was she like, this woman reporter from Philadelphia? Was she hard and brittle? So brittle, so sharp, that she would tear Royke's heart in two?

"Go to bed, you imaginative old fool," Cassie muttered aloud as she turned in the direction of her own quarters.

While Cassie was occupied with her mental journey into the past, Stacy was grappling with the present. With Sandi's warning about the bed in mind, Stacy had slid gingerly between the sheets, only to be pleasantly surprised at how comfortable the narrow cot was. Yet, snuggled beneath the covers for warmth against the cold spring night, she found herself unable to fall asleep because of disturbing thoughts of Royke Larson.

Uncomfortable in her mind, Stacy shifted position on the cot, only to turn back again a moment later. Why did Royke look at her with such contempt in his eyes? It was as if he considered her too superficial, too shallow, to be worth knowing. She certainly did not consider herself shallow. At least, not as far as intellect was concerned, but, as to life-style...

Stacy's eyes flew open as she shot upright on the bed. Was her life-style banal and pointless? Did anybody really *care* about what the people she interviewed thought? Did she?

She cared about what *he* thought.

Good God! The realization was both enlightening and frightening. With the bright clarity that often came to her late in the night,

Stacy recognized in herself the symptoms of
an age-old malady. She was bored to distrac-
tion with her life. And that explained her un-
settled, dissatisfied feelings of the previous
few weeks.

Damn! Her whole life had become a sham.
She was doing work she no longer liked or
believed in. She was seeing friends she no
longer respected. She was obeying a mother
she no longer honored.

One day, Stacy moaned inwardly. One day
away from the familiar, and the truth had
come crashing down on her. A disturbing image rose to the forefront of her mind, and
Stacy gritted her teeth in anger. In some in-
explicable way Royke Larson had exposed
her compromise with life.

Disturbing? Royke Larson was much more
than disturbing. To Stacy he was downright
dangerous!

"You are in trouble here, Stacy," she muttered aloud. "Get this interview over with in
a hurry and get out of here."

Pounding the pillow into a shapeless mess,
Stacy burrowed into it and shut her eyes tight,
willing herself into the sweet escape of sleep.

Fortunately for her, the sheer length of the day had exhausted her; within minutes Stacy was out like a light.

The children woke her much too early the next morning. They did not invade the privacy of her room, nor were they exceptionally noisy in the hallway. In fact, it was their murmuring attempt to be quiet that woke her, which proved one thing as far as she was concerned: she hadn't been sleeping too deeply in the first place!

Seconds after Stacy opened her eyes, a small smile curved the sleep-softened fullness of her lips. The two oldest Case children were trying so hard to be quiet while getting ready for school.

"Laura, will you hurry it up a little? I've got to use the bathroom," whispered young Mike.

"I gotta brush my teeth, don't I?" Laura wailed.

"Aw, gee!" Mike Jr.'s voice faded as his small feet stamped along the hallway. "Mom!" Stacy heard him cry.

Her smile growing, Stacy pushed back the

down comforter and swung her legs to the floor. What a nice sound to wake up to, she thought, stretching as she stood up. The only sound she ever heard upon awakening was the muted noise of the early-morning rush-hour traffic on the street six stories below her bedroom window. Her mother's apartment was always serenely quiet, and quite often deadly depressing.

Another new sound drew Stacy to the room's one window, which faced the large barn and fenced corral at the back of the house. Drawing the sheers away from the windowpane, Stacy glanced around in an effort to locate the chattering birds that had caught her attention. There they were, in a tree not far from the house. A family perhaps? she mused. They were fluttering around busily, doing whatever birds do early in the morning.

How absolutely ignorant you are about nature and its small creatures, she chided herself in amusement. Without conceit Stacy knew that were someone to ask her about any one of a hundred prominent women, she could correctly rattle off a mind-boggling number of facts and figures. But when it came to wildlife, Stacy was a total washout, and she knew it.

"Well, it's about time!" Mike Jr. exclaimed in an aggrieved tone. Letting the sheer curtain fall back into place, Stacy strained her ears to hear Laura's response.

"If you'd get up when Mom calls you instead of sticking your head under the covers, you could get into the bathroom first. So it's your own fault if you have to wait."

"Girls are nuts!" Mike Jr. shouted, forgetting himself and the need for quiet.

Chuckling softly, Stacy made the bed, then withdrew a pair of jeans and a tailored shirt from the room's one tiny closet. She was taking fresh underwear from the top dresser drawer when she heard Mike Jr. vacate the bathroom, still muttering about the burden of having a younger sister.

While she showered, then dressed, Stacy wondered what it was like to wake each and every morning to the sometimes happy, sometimes quarrelsome exchange of youngsters. Pulling a brush through her rebellious short curls, she grinned at her reflection, de-

ciding that being around young children was
no doubt a mixed blessing.

Sandi probably experiences days when
she'd like to chuck it all and run for the hills,
Stacy concluded as she strode along the hall
to the living room. But then, doesn't everyone
experience days like that? she thought,
crossing the living room to the strangely silent kitchen.

On entering the cheerfully bright kitchen,
Stacy found Sandi sitting at the table enjoying
a cup of coffee. As soon as the other woman
saw her she grinned serenely.

"Do you hear it?" Sandi asked softly.

"Hear what?" Though she strained her
ears, Stacy couldn't detect a sound.

"The silence." Sandi sighed. "Isn't it
beautiful?" She closed her eyes as if in ecstasy. "I have approximately thirty minutes
to enjoy it before my little terror wakes up."

Was she hearing the muted cry of discontent? A ripple of unease slithered through
Stacy. Guarding her expression, Stacy accepted the cup of coffee Sandi offered her.
Why should she feel disappointed? she asked
herself fleetingly. Hadn't she been expecting

this underlying discontent? She had. Of course, she had believed she'd have to root it out of Sandi with carefully worded questions. Why then this sense of sharp disappointment?

"What would you like for breakfast?"

Sandi's query nudged Stacy out of her reverie. Faking a yawn to indicate she was still half asleep, Stacy smiled warmly at her hostess. "Toast, juice—" she shrugged "—whatever. I'm really not a breakfast person."

"I'd hazard a guess you are not an early-morning person, either," Sandi teased, returning the smile.

Stacy's soft laughter floated lightly through the sunshine-bright room. "Well, not *this* early. I usually roll out of bed about an hour later than this."

"Good grief!" Sandi pretended shock. "I've been up for nearly two hours already! What an indolent bunch you city girls are." She set a glass of what looked like freshly squeezed orange juice in front of Stacy, then planted her hands on her hips. "But, do you know what? I wouldn't trade places with you for anything."

"Really?" Stacy breathed a silent sigh of

relief; Sandi obviously was not discontent
with her lot. Though Stacy told herself that
the wave of satisfaction sweeping through her
was unwarranted, she could not deny the feeling. "Don't you ever get the urge to chuck it
all?" The interview had begun. Stacy knew
it, and Sandi knew it, too.

"This is for the record, isn't it?" Sandi
arched one well-shaped brow quizzically as
she slid a plate of toast across the table to
Stacy.

"Yes," Stacy answered honestly. Then,
grinning, she added, "But I'd like you to hold
your answer until I've finished eating. I didn't
bring my tape recorder and notebook with
me."

"Whenever." Sandi shrugged, grinning
back. "As long as you don't mind following
me around while I do my work."

"Mmm..." Stacy shook her head in response, chewing a bite of toast. After swallowing, she explained. "I want you to go
about your daily routine as always."

After finishing her breakfast, Stacy went to
her room to collect her small tape recorder,
her notebook, and a pen. Returning to the

kitchen, she found Sandi busy putting it in
order. Thus commenced what Stacy would
forever after remember as a marathon. Sandi
quite willingly answered each and every one
of Stacy's questions, elaborating on many of
them without hesitation.

And all the while they talked, Sandi was
on the move. She had no sooner finished in
the kitchen when young David, looking bright
eyed, bushy tailed, and absolutely adorable in
his Doctor Dentons, padded into the room
with a sweet-voiced demand for breakfast.

Stacy sipped another cup of coffee, firing
questions at Sandi as the woman prepared her
son's meal, kept a sharp eye on him while he
consumed it, then began the cleaning-up process all over again. The marathon continued
as Sandi went nonstop from one chore to another until lunchtime. Her tape recorder
clutched in her hand, Stacy followed in
Sandi's wake.

"Where were you born?"

"Right here in Montana."

"On a ranch such as this one?"

"No." Sandi paused in her bed making to

grin at Stacy. "Actually, I'm a city girl like you. I was born and raised in Billings."

"Then you weren't accustomed to ranch life before your marriage to Mike?" Stacy continued, trailing Sandi through the house and into the backyard.

"Hardly," Sandi drawled, mixing feed grains together in a bucket. "I worked in an insurance office." Again her grin flashed as she fed the grain to some noisy chickens. "I was an excellent private secretary if I do say so myself." She bent down to allow David a handful of the mixture to scatter to the birds. "I met Mike on a blind date," she continued, supplying the answer to Stacy's next question before Stacy had a chance to ask it. Narrowing her eyes, Sandi examined a plot of land off to the side of the chicken pens. "It'll soon be time to get the rows ready for planting," she mused.

"Planting?" Stacy frowned. "What are you going to plant?"

"Vegetables." Sandi laughed. "The peas we had for a side dish last night?" Her eyebrows arched.

"Yes, they were delicious." Stacy understood. "You grew them?"

"And froze them," Sandi said. "I grow most of the vegetables we eat." An impish smile lit her face. "I kill two birds with one stone...or hoe, if you will. In the summer I work in the garden in halter and shorts, and so I acquire a tan while tending the veggies." Turning back to the house, she added, "Lying in the sun by a pool, doing nothing, always bored the hell out of me."

Laughing with her, Stacy stepped carefully over the winter-hardened ground, drawing the jacket she'd thrown over her shoulders closer against the chill wind; it might be spring back East, she thought, shivering, but somebody forgot to inform Montana!

The minute their jackets were stashed away in the laundry room off the kitchen, Sandi plopped David down with a box of building blocks, then proceeded to empty the washer of the clothes she'd loaded into it before trooping into the yard.

"How long did you know Mike before you and he married?" Stacy asked while Sandi transferred the wet clothes to the dryer.

The dryer door closed with a snap and Sandi straightened to face Stacy, a glimmer of amusement dancing in her eyes. "Two weeks to the day," she replied candidly.

"Two weeks?" Stacy repeated incredulously.

"Two weeks," a masculine voice responded.

Spinning around, Stacy felt her breath catch at the sight of the tall man leaning indolently against the doorframe. In tight, worn jeans, scuffed boots, a rather battered Stetson and a denim jacket with the wide collar turned up around his neck and jaw, Royke Larson looked rugged, ready for anything, and altogether far too attractive.

Chapter Five

"I should know. I had to listen to Mike rave on and on about the woman of his dreams for the entire two weeks."

Pushing himself erect, Royke brought two fingers to the brim of his Stetson in a gesture of respect. "And how are you ladies today?" he inquired softly. Before either of the women could respond, he observed, "Into the interview, I see."

"Yes, we are." Laughing softly, Sandi walked to him. "And we're both fine, thank you." Sliding her arms around his waist, she gave him a quick hug. "I didn't expect to see you today.'' Tilting her head, she gazed up at him with an expression bordering on adoration. ''To what do we owe this honor?''

Royke's soft chuckle sent a jolt of electricity the length of Stacy's spine. God! she mused, unabashedly staring at him. This man's potency is darn near tangible! Stacy had the whimsical notion that if she should reach out her hand, she would actually feel the sexuality that radiated from Royke. Shivering slightly from the realization of the power Royke possessed, Stacy lowered her eyes when he raised his, positive that what she'd encounter in those dark depths would be mocking laughter—laughter aimed at her!

''I brought the wagon back,'' Royke's low tone did indeed hold amusement.

Feeling in some way challenged, Stacy flung her head back to face his mockery head-on. One well-shaped brow arched arrogantly, and Stacy had the uncanny feeling she could read his mind. And what he was thinking, she guessed, was that she was ineffectual, insignificant, and unimportant.

''Will you stay for lunch?'' Sandi asked, bestowing her most beguiling smile on him.

No! Stacy cried silently.

"Yes." Royke answered softly.

"Good." Disengaging herself, Sandi turned to David, who'd toddled up to hang on to Royke's leg. "You probably couldn't have escaped anyway." She laughed. "At least not without dragging your godchild along." Hoisting the boy to her hip, she sailed into the kitchen, leaving Stacy to stand there, uncomfortably staring at the man she knew to be her enemy.

"You don't like me, do you?" Royke murmured, smiling derisively.

"I don't know you!" Shaken by his directness, Stacy blurted out the first thing that came to mind. "Nor do you know me." Drawing a calming breath, she added, "But I feel you don't like me."

"Not much," Royke admitted blandly. "But, more important, I don't trust you." Stepping close to her, he growled, "I'm giving you fair warning. If you hurt Sandi in any way with this stupid article you're doing, you will answer to me." Now the smile that curved his lips could be described only as feral. "And I can be very, very nasty when I'm angry."

"Hey, you two!" Sandi's call covered the gasp that escaped Stacy. "Lunch is on the table."

"Coming," Royke called back pleasantly. Then, bending down until his nose almost touched hers, he snarled, "Do you understand, *Ms.* Ernshaw?"

The contrast between the light tone with which he'd answered Sandi and the lethal sound of his voice as he issued his warning to her caused a shudder along Stacy's entire body. But refusing to give in, Stacy drew herself up to her full five feet three inches and informed him chillingly, "I'm not afraid of *you!* What could you possibly do to *me?*"

Royke's answering smile was so blatantly sexual, it took Stacy's breath away. As she opened her mouth to gulp in air, he struck like a poised rattler, clamping his lips to hers as he caught her to him in a crushing embrace.

Stacy had heard and read about the kiss that destroys. A true skeptic, she had never dreamed she'd experience it. Unable to respond or even move, she remained motionless against his hard chest, feeling the deepening kiss sear through her like a flame.

Shaken by the heat suffusing her body, Stacy was passive while Royke's mouth devoured hers. And *devoured* was the only word that applied to what he was doing.

Beginning to feel light-headed, Stacy conceded that, yes, Royke could be very, very nasty when he was angered. She was hanging on to consciousness by sheer will when Sandi, unaware of her guest's plight, called from the adjacent room.

"What *are* you two doing? The salad is starting to wilt."

Taking his time, Royke slowly released Stacy's mouth. As he raised his head, a knowing smile lifted the corners of his lips. Though Stacy had not responded directly to his kiss, her body had quickened to sensual life. Only a blatant fool would not have felt the need quivering through her slender form; and Royke Larson was far from a fool.

"Now, what was your question?" he taunted softly. "Ah, yes. What could I possibly do to you?" Stepping away from her,

he ran an all-encompassing glance over her
small, still-trembling frame. He smiled sardonically. "Many, many different things, Ms.
Ernshaw. All of which would be entertaining
for me but, from your horrified expression,
I'm sure they would be humiliating for you."
Suddenly his face became a mask of cold dis-
dain. "As I said before, don't, in any way,
hurt her." As if dismissing her from his consideration, Royke turned his back to her and
sauntered into the kitchen, his tone easy as he
began teasing both Sandi and her youngest
child.

Staring at the empty doorway, Stacy bit her
lip in an attempt to contain the tremors shaking her body. Distractedly lifting one hand,
she massaged her stomach, which had begun
burning again. Never had Stacy felt so mor-
tified. All she wanted to do was run to the
guest room and hide until Royke had left the
property.

The desire to creep away appalled her.
What was she? A modern, liberated woman
or a shrinking Victorian miss, easily put in
her place?

Ignoring the fact that her own mother could

put her in her place with a quelling look, Stacy assured herself she could take anything Royke Larson could dish out, and hand it back to him tenfold.

Her confidence restored, Stacy strolled into the kitchen, a bright smile plastered onto her lips.

"Ah, there you are." Sandi glanced up at Stacy from her stooping position in front of the refrigerator. "What were you doing in the laundry room for so long?"

"I...ah...was watching those dark clouds out the window." Stacy grasped at the excuse, waving her hand toward the window and the storm clouds she'd noticed before entering the house with Sandi a short time ago. "They've obliterated the mountaintops."

Straightening, Sandi gave the clouds a brief glance before closing the refrigerator door. "Rain, I hope," she predicted.

On the other side of the room Royke was busy putting David onto his high stool. After sliding the stool up to the table, Royke raised mocking eyes to Stacy's, his sardonic smile telling her he knew better.

"Then again, those clouds could be carrying snow," he said. "A spring blizzard is not unusual in Montana."

"A blizzard?" Stacy asked, spinning around to stare with real interest at the slow-moving front.

"Hmm, could tie things up around here for as long as a week," Royke concurred. "People get stranded for days," he added softly, his eyes narrow as he watched for her reaction.

Stacy didn't disappoint him. She spun around to face the windows. Stranded for days! Stacy shuddered. She'd go stir-crazy in hours, she felt sure, were she confined within while a blizzard raged outside. Born and raised in a large city, where the populace considered even the worst snowstorms a messy inconvenience, Stacy had never had her movements curtailed for more than a few hours; she might have to walk, but she got around. She knew without being told that out here things would be quite different.

Frowning at the overcast sky, Stacy was unaware that Royke had come near until he spoke softly right behind her.

"Perhaps it would be wise for you to finish

the interview quickly, then catch the next plane east," he suggested, voicing her own thought.

"Royke Larson!" Though Royke's voice had been low, Sandi had obviously heard his advice. "Will you stop teasing Stacy!" Turning to face her, they found her with her hands on her hips and a grin tilting her lips. "Really, Stacy, the weather bureau has issued no warning of a blizzard." As she made the assurance, Sandi indicated the table. "If we don't eat soon, the soup will be cool and the dessert will be warm."

All the while she sipped the delicious homemade beef-barley soup, Stacy cast surreptitious glances at the slate gray sky until, turning her head quickly, she caught the twitch of amusement playing over Royke's lips.

The devious rat! Stacy fumed, realizing that she'd been set up. Royke wanted to be rid of her. What better way to evict her than to scare her off? Why was Royke so eager to see the back of her? Stacy wondered, stoically eating her lunch. Why, because he feared she'd in some way injure his lady-love, she concluded nastily. What an absolute bore people were when they became emotionally involved, she thought wearily.

But were they involved—really involved? Or was this a one-sided infatuation on Royke's part? Tantalized by the question, Stacy glanced from Royke to Sandi, and concentrated on their conversation.

"...packed him a lunch." Sandi was explaining Mike's absence from the table. "He'll probably be mending fences till dark."

"I'll go hunt him up and give him a hand as soon as I've finished here," Royke offered, then added very casually, "Oh, by the way, I had Skeeter check out the wagon this morning. It's running all right now."

"Oh, Royke." Sandi sighed. "That wasn't necessary." Seeing Stacy's interest, Sandi explained. "Skeeter Colton is Royke's handyman and mechanic. He takes care of all the mechanized equipment." Frowning darkly, Sandi returned her attention to Royke. "I was going to take the wagon into the garage later this week."

"Or next week," Royke drawled. "Or the week after."

Sandi's laughter seemed to bounce around the cheery room. "You know me too well, Mr. Larson," she agreed.

"Precisely, Mrs. Case." Royke's tone was devoid of humor. "And I do not consider it a laughing matter. You were taking your life in your hands every time you drove that thing in the condition it was in."

Taking advantage of the fact that Royke's full attention was centered on Sandi, Stacy studied his harsh features openly. In Stacy's opinion, Royke's chastisement of Sandi spoke volumes about his feelings for her. For some reason this confirmation of what Stacy had suspected caused a strangely empty sensation inside her.

Caught up in her own speculation, Stacy was deaf to the murmur of Sandi's reply to Royke's scolding. Stacy's mind rebelled at the image of Royke embracing Sandi, kissing Sandi the way he had kissed her such a short time ago.

This is ridiculous, she told herself scathingly. You do not believe in the concept of romantic love, let alone the myth of wild, overwhelming, instantaneous physical attraction!

But then, how to explain the near violent anger coursing through her entire system in reaction to the mere idea of Royke and Sandi together?

As Stacy looked past the veneer of civilization to the basic woman beneath, she found her explanation: In Royke Larson she recognized her masculine counterpart, her mate. She didn't like it, but there it was: Stacy Ernshaw craved Royke Larson!

"I want to get down!"

Young David's shrill demand pierced Stacy's introspection. Blinking as if coming awake, she focused on the couple seated across the table from her. Royke, his face alight with indulgent laughter, had switched his attention from Sandi to his godchild. Sandi, her expression serene, was rising to clear the lunch plates.

"You're beginning to give orders like a top-notch ramrod, cowboy," Royke teased as he scooped the wriggling child off the stool and into his arms.

Incredibly, Stacy found herself wishing it were she, and not the little boy, being held in Royke's arms. Smothering a gasp of dismay, she jumped to her feet and began gathering up dishes and flatware.

This is utterly crazy! You don't even like the man! As she moved back and forth between the table and the sink, Stacy took herself to task. There is absolutely no reason whatever for feeling envy for the mother, but to experience it for the child, that's sheer madness!

"You were very quiet all through lunch, Stacy," Sandi observed. "Surely you're not worrying about the weather?"

"Yes, a little." Stacy grasped at the excuse. Here was her chance to hastily complete the interview and remove herself from Royke's disturbing presence. Stacy formed her plans even as she voiced them.

"I'm going to call the airport to see if I can get connections back East for tomorrow morning." Though Sandi squawked in protest, Stacy continued. "I can't afford to take the chance, no matter how slight, of being stranded. Of course, I want to complete the

interview.'' Here she paused to smile appeal-
ingly at Sandi. ''If we concentrate, and stay
at it, I feel positive I can gather enough material for the article.'' As Stacy concluded,
she glanced at Royke and immediately
wished she hadn't. The upward tilt of his lips
was a dead giveaway. Royke Larson most decidedly wanted her long gone!

Sandi's reaction was an altogether different
story. She was quick to verbalize her dissatisfaction.

''But, Stacy!'' she cried. ''You said you
were going to be here at least three, possibly
four days! And we've been getting along so
well. Please, reconsider your deci—''

''Ms. Ernshaw has stated her desire to go,
Sandi,'' Royke interrupted with quiet force.
''If she can not *afford* the time, then that's all
there is to it.''

Sandi glanced at Royke in obvious disappointment. Stacy glared at him in sudden
fury. He had deliberately twisted her words
against her. In misinterpreting her plea, he
had conveyed to Sandi the idea that Stacy was
merely bored, and itching to get back to the
big city. In truth, Stacy was not at all bored

by Sandi or her family. In fact, except for
Royke's appearance, she had been enjoying
herself immensely ever since the children
woke her early that morning.

Though it galled her to do so, Stacy swallowed the sharp denial that sprang to her lips.
She *did* want to go, and the sooner the better.
Let them think what they would. Containing
her anger, Stacy contrived a coolly withdrawn
smile.

"I'm sorry, Sandi, but I really do have a
full schedule, and a delay of only one day
would wreak havoc with it." Though Stacy
was determined to go, she was equally determined to hang on to the budding friendship
between herself and Sandi. Stepping close to
the other woman, Stacy ignored the mocking
disbelief mirrored on Royke's face and appealed to Sandi.

"I would have enjoyed the opportunity to
get to know you better, but I really can't
stay." Impulsively, she placed her hand on
Sandi's. "Will you cooperate with me on the
article?"

Though Sandi sighed, she also smiled. "Of
course I'll cooperate, you nit!" She spun

around to frown at Royke. "I thought you were going to give Mike a hand?" she chided Royke, reaching for her sleepy-eyed son. "Take off, neighbor. I'm going to dump this little love into bed for a nap. Then Stacy and I have work to do."

Relinquishing his hold on the boy, Royke favored Sandi with the tender smile that now slashed at Stacy's heart. "I'm going, I'm going," he said lightly, then ruined Stacy's relief by adding, "But be careful what you say. I'm sure everything will be duly noted." Slicing a glance at Stacy, he again smiled tauntingly.

Stacy had to work at squashing the urge to slap his arrogant face. Cautioning herself against being stupid, she snatched David from Sandi's arms. "Please, let me put him to bed for you," she begged.

"Unlike some—" Sandi looked pointedly at Royke "—I never look a gift horse in the mouth."

Eager to put distance between herself and Royke, Stacy clasped the child more firmly in her arms and headed for the living room. As she strode through the archway she heard

Sandi invite Royke to dinner in payment for his help. Out of sight of the other two, she paused to catch Royke's response, silently groaning when it came.

"Worded like that, how can I refuse?" Then he asked, "Will you call Cassie and tell her I won't be home for dinner?"

Who the devil is Cassie? Stacy wondered as she walked to the hallway and the bedrooms beyond. Wife? Housekeeper? Mistress? Uncomfortably aware that only one of the three roles would be acceptable to her, Stacy ordered herself to forget Royke and concentrate on David.

In actuality David needed very little concentration, for he was asleep almost before Stacy had removed his boots and jeans. Still, Stacy hesitated by the child's bed, gazing down at the sweet face of the sleeping child.

For the first time in her adult life Stacy wondered what it would be like to care for a tiny human she had nurtured inside her body. Startled by the thought, yet unable to ignore it, she pictured an infant with brown hair and brown eyes, and the look of sturdiness that comes from living close to the land.

Thoroughly shaken by her imagination, Stacy hurried from the room. Whatever could be the matter with her? Physical attraction to Royke she could contend with. But picturing what his child might look like, well, that she could in no way handle. Oh, yes, it was definitely time to go home.

Returning to the kitchen, Stacy found Sandi up to her elbows in dishwater. Plucking a dish towel from the rack above the sink, she began drying and interviewing simultaneously.

The questioning ceased as the children burst into the house after school. But it commenced again after they'd been given a snack and had dispersed to their rooms to do whatever children do in their rooms. Even David, who had happily followed Stacy and his mother wherever they went throughout the afternoon, trailed in his brother's footsteps.

Several times during the day Stacy caught herself on the point of asking Sandi about Royke. What, she demanded of herself, could she possibly ask Sandi? She certainly could not bluntly inquire if Royke was the other woman's lover, for heaven's sake, even if she did long to know the answer to that question above all others.

By dinnertime Stacy was too familiar with Sandi's casual attitude to life to be surprised when Sandi hugged both Mike and Royke with equal fervor when they padded into the kitchen in their stocking feet. And she gave only a mental shrug when Royke announced his intention of having a shower before dinner.

Sitting down to dinner with three very vocal children was another new experience for Stacy. Whenever she dined at the home of friends with children, the kids were always tucked neatly out of the way before the adults sat down to the table.

Stacy found that the experience was fun, and not a trial at all. Nor did the presence of the children curtail the adults' conversation. In fact, the entire meal proceeded pleasantly, and ended all too quickly.

To Stacy's surprise Royke and Mike offered to supervise the kids' baths while Sandi and Stacy cleaned up in the kitchen. Staring in wonder, she watched as the men herded the youngsters out of the room.

"Why the stupefied look?"

Swinging back to Sandi, Stacy shook her head. "Somehow I would never imagine Royke in the role of nursemaid," she admitted frankly.

"Whyever not?" Sandi exclaimed. "Royke loves kids, especially mine, owing to the fact that he sees more of them than any others. He'll make a wonderful father..." She frowned. "If there lives a woman who can ever drag him to the altar."

"Then he's not married?"

Tilting her head, Sandi gave Stacy a quizzical look. "Of course he's not married! Do you really think he'd have stayed for dinner two nights running if he were?"

"I don't know." Stacy shrugged lightly. "I know several married men who seldom have dinner at home."

"Sounds like a dumb way to conduct a marriage, if you ask me." With that, Sandi attacked the dishes in the sink.

Taking up the towel, Stacy again began her probing of the "professional" housewife, who had already gained her respect.

"And what is your idea of a smart way to conduct a marriage?" she asked softly.

"Together," Sandi said succinctly. Her hands stilled as she turned a level gaze on Stacy. "I mean, why bother to get married in the first place if you have no intention of being together? Doesn't it kind of defeat the whole purpose?"

My question exactly, Stacy thought wryly. Then, in all fairness, she felt she had to defend the men she'd mentioned.

"Understand," she began slowly, "these people I know who see little of each other during the week spend most of the weekend together and, of course, vacation time." Usually, she amended silently, reflecting on the couples she knew who always took separate vacations.

"Oh, terrific!" Sandi jeered. "A weekend-and-the-occasional-vacation marriage. I love it!" Suddenly serious, her lips tightened. "Their kids must love it, too."

Feeling in some strange way threatened herself, Stacy doggedly carried on the defense. "But, Sandi, you don't understand. These people I'm referring to pursue very busy lives. They have careers to see to, and a living to earn.''

"So have Mike and I," Sandi reminded her gently. "In Mike's case, this ranch is his career, and in mine, it's my family. Personally, I wouldn't change places with any other woman." Shaking her head slightly, she said, "For myself, I can't imagine any job more important than looking after Mike and caring for our children. *That's* the career that feels natural to me. But—" Sandi smiled "—different strokes for different folks, I guess."

There wasn't a shred of doubt in Stacy's mind of Sandi's sincerity. Against all the odds, Sandi Case was proving to be every bit the professional homemaker her friend had claimed she was. But, as Stacy was learning to her surprise and delight, she was finding much, much more in Sandi. If she had to put it into concrete terms, the only thing Stacy could come up with was *soul mate*.

"Are you trying to rub the pattern off the plate?"

"I was mulling over what you said." Grinning, Stacy carefully placed the plate on top of the neat pile in the cabinet above the sink.

"And?" Sandi prompted her.

"I've decided you're a pretty special lady," Stacy said candidly.

"Oh, heavens, *I* knew that!" Though Sandi's tone was lofty, it was evident to Stacy that her compliment had flustered the older woman. Her expression suddenly quite serious, Sandi confided, "You know, from the moment you introduced yourself to me I felt a…a…" She fluttered the fingers of one hand as if attempting to draw words from thin air. "Oh, I don't know, a…bond, or something, between us." Now Sandi gave a helpless shrug. "Do you have any idea at all what I'm trying to say?"

"Sisters in spirit if not in blood?" Stacy offered hopefully.

"Yes!" Sandi sighed in relief. "Exactly that." Again her shoulders rose in a shrug. "It's odd, but I feel closer to you than to other women I've known all my life." A bubble of laughter escaped her smiling lips. "Maybe there's something to the theory of reincarnation, after all!"

"You mean we may actually have been sisters during a prior lifetime?" Stacy suggested, beginning to chuckle as Sandi's humor struck her.

"Or comrades-in-arms!" Sandi gasped, shaking with laughter.

"Or coconspirators in some dark and devious plot!" Stacy whispered dramatically, caught up in the fun of it now, and giggling like a teenager.

"Mike, I think we've got a real problem here. It would appear that these two females have gone completely bananas!"

Later, when she was alone in the small guest room, Stacy reflected that the scene Royke had witnessed on entering the kitchen would have led anybody to the conclusion that she and Sandi had indeed "gone completely bananas." But, Lord, it *had* been pure fun to laugh again with such innocent glee.

Chapter Six

A very unusual state of confusion made Royke restless as he lay in his huge bed. It had been after eleven when he'd finally taken his leave of the Cases and their beautiful, but disturbing, guest.

Frowning into the darkness, Royke tried to sort out his conflicting emotions. Stacy was leaving in the morning, and he was glad she was going. Yet, at the same time, he found himself longing for her to stay. The way he was feeling didn't make any sense, and that unnerved him; if nothing else, Royke prided himself on his common sense.

It was common sense that had made him uneasy about her in the first place. Yet Stacy Ernshaw simply would not fit into the slot where he wanted to put her.

Royke had formed a mental image of Stacy from the minute Sandi had informed him about the forthcoming interview. At the time, he had not bothered to imagine what the reporter's outward appearance would be; to Royke, it was the inner qualities that mattered. And he had convinced himself that Sandi would be facing a woman with the personality of a viper.

Shifting restlessly on the now-disheveled bed, Royke experienced again the sensations of protectiveness and compassion he'd felt when he'd seen Stacy on the plane. At that time—was it really only yesterday?—he had felt an overwhelming urge to draw her slight form into the haven of his embrace. Now, after the disillusionment of discovering exactly who and what she was, Royke admitted to himself that he still wanted to draw her into his arms, but for altogether different reasons.

Damn! Suddenly warm, he flipped onto his back and kicked the covers to the foot of the bed. The sweat beading his forehead was not generated by the excellent heating system he'd installed a few years back; no, his active imagination was the source of the heat coursing through his entire body.

Shaken by the very intensity of that heat, Royke groaned aloud into the silence of the room. Alone, and to himself, Royke faced the unpalatable fact that he wanted Stacy Ernshaw in a way that was almost frightening. But, more frightening still was the realization that he wanted Stacy to want *him* with equal fervor. And, judging from Stacy's attitude toward him, Royke figured he had about as much hope of having his longing fulfilled as he had of seeing his herds of prime beef stock performing a break dance.

"Oh, damn and blast!"

Even as Royke muttered his frustration, another sound made an impact on his consciousness. Rain! It was raining! An instant after Royke heard the sharp ping against his window, the meaning of the sound burst into his mind.

Sure as morning would come, it would arrive coated with ice! Royke had felt it in the air as he drove through the night on his way home; he'd known that if there was rain, it would be freezing rain. He had also known that if there was freezing rain, chances were Stacy would not be flying anywhere.

Damn!

The conflict was back, blanking out all else. Royke was at once elated and depressed; he wanted her to leave with what amounted to desperation. He wanted her to stay with equal fervor.

While listening to the beating sound of the rain upon his window, Royke experienced the sensation of being pulled in two directions, for while part of him hoped the rain would cease, another part prayed that it would continue.

Sitting cross-legged in the middle of the small bed, Stacy also heard the rain striking her window. The sound was meaningless to her. In comparison to the confusion tearing at her mind, what importance could a little rain have?

At that moment the weather, or the inconvenience it could possibly cause her, was the farthest thing from Stacy's mind. Royke Larson occupied all her attention.

Frowning in concentration, Stacy reviewed the events of the evening from the moment Royke had made his amused observation: "Mike, I think we've got a real problem here. It would appear that these two females have gone completely bananas!"

Royke's exclamation had sent Stacy and Sandi into gales of laughter. Though their laughter had been out of proportion to the incident, their mirth had been thoroughly satisfying. When it had subsided, both women felt mellow and ready for the coffee and dessert Sandi had promised the men as a reward for taking over the children's bath-and-bedtime routine.

They had ensconced themselves comfortably in front of an aromatic crackling fire, Sandi and Mike side by side on the well-worn sofa, Stacy and Royke opposite them on deep, cushiony easy chairs. The tray bearing the coffee and dessert sat on the long coffee table separating them.

"I don't know, ol' buddy," Mike mused after Royke had questioned the two women to no avail. "But I have this nasty suspicion that neither one of these charming ladies is about to let us in on the joke." Languidly raising his hand, he smoothed his wife's raven dark hair.

Strangely, the very familiarity of the act touched a chord deep inside Stacy, causing a humming sensation through her veins. Silently, she echoed the almost inaudible sigh that whispered through Sandi's smiling lips.

"I suppose you're right." Royke helped himself to a thick slice of devil's food cake as he concurred lazily, surprising Stacy with his apparent unconcern over the way Mike was now blatantly caressing his wife's cheek with his fingertips.

Her smile widening to a grin, Sandi snuggled closer to Mike. "There was no joke, really," she protested. "Stacy and I were just being silly."

"Ms. Ernshaw being silly? I find that improbable, if not downright impossible." Royke looked at Stacy in amazement. "I would have bet my favorite horse that there was not a frivolous bone in Stacy's small but neatly put together body."

In the motion of carrying the mug in her hand to her mouth, Stacy's arm went still in midair. She was momentarily caught without a rejoinder, but Sandi made it for her.

"Then you would have lost the horse," she declared complacently. "I assure you, Stacy was being as silly as a giddy teenager."

"How interesting." Royke didn't appear at all interested as he attacked the rich-looking cake on his plate. Chewing thoughtfully, he stared at Stacy speculatively. Then, washing the cake down with a deep swallow of coffee, he mused aloud, "What other interesting facets are there in Stacy's character, I wonder?" One eyebrow arched. "You're among friends, Stacy. Feel like letting your hair down—" he grinned as his gaze fell on her cropped curls "—so to speak?"

"I think not," Stacy demurred, caught between a frown of disapproval and a reciprocal grin.

"Ignore Royke, Stacy." Mike offered the advice sagely. "He does love teasing the ladies."

"I'll say!" Sandi laughed. "And he's had so darn much practice, too!"

Seeing her chance to retaliate, Stacy drawled, "You're a big ladies' man on the range?"

Amazingly, Royke's grin held genuine amusement. "I've...ah...known a few," he confessed, dryly.

"In the biblical sense?" Stacy matched his dry tone exactly.

Sandi howled with delight. Mike choked on a swallow of coffee. Royke's eyes gleamed with appreciation of her sally.

"I never kiss, or anything else, and tell, Ms. Ernshaw." The gleam of appreciation darkened to a glitter of breathtaking sensuality. "In that area you have nothing to fear from me."

He was no doubt referring to his kiss in the laundry that afternoon, Stacy mused. "How very reassuring," she murmured, lowering her eyes demurely, yet feeling oddly excited by the verbal exchange. She was flirting, actually flirting with the man, and she wasn't even sure yet if she liked him!

Raising her eyes slowly to his, Stacy felt a shock go down her spine. Royke Larson was flirting with her! The deepening color of his eyes and the sensuous curve of his lips left her in little doubt about it.

"Now, what the devil is that supposed to mean?" Sandi asked, her gaze swinging from Royke to Stacy. "Does he have something to tell about?"

While Stacy raked her mind for a noncommittal reply, Royke took over.

"Sandi, please refer back to what I just said."

Sandi's face went totally blank, then she frowned, but before she could demand an explanation, Mike stole the initiative from her.

"I think, my love, that you've just been told politely to mind your own business."

"Well, really!" Sandi affected shock. "And in my own home, too! What do you have to say for yourself, Mr. Larson?"

"The cake is delicious. How are my chances for getting seconds?"

Royke's bantering tone set the mood for the rest of the evening. The conversation flowed easily among the four of them, creating an ambience of camaraderie.

Talking more freely than she often did with friends of many years, Stacy gave them a thumbnail sketch of life in the city, playing up the cultural advantages while minimizing the drawbacks. Royke was the only one to question Stacy on the latter.

"You will concede that it's not safe for a woman to be on the street alone after dark, though, won't you?" He taunted her softly.

"Certainly." Stacy nodded her head obligingly. Then, as Royke's smile grew smug, she added sweetly, "But then, I'd suggest that it's unsafe for a woman to be outside alone after dark almost anywhere in the world, wouldn't *you?*"

"Pack it in, friend," Mike advised laughingly. "She has a zinger for you every time you try baiting her."

"Point taken." Lifting the can of beer Mike had provided moments before, Royke tilted it in a silent salute to Stacy.

Feeling ridiculously as though she'd won a war instead of a minor skirmish, Stacy murmured, "Now, suppose you tell me about the life-style out here." Suddenly realizing that she was speaking solely to him, Stacy turned quickly to include Sandi and Mike in her request.

Even though Stacy was attentive as her three companions took turns giving her a brief outline of their lives, a corner of her mind remained busy storing up impressions of Royke.

With her reporter's instincts, Stacy asked incisive questions, while another, purely feminine part of her filed away impressions of his height, the breadth of his shoulders, the slimness of his waist and hips, the long, taut musculature of his thighs. Into her memory went a recording of the angles and planes that made up his distinctive features: the broad hands and slender fingers with their sprinkling of dark hairs; the dark eyes that could gleam with amusement or glitter with annoyance.

By the time the impromptu party broke up, Stacy had unconsciously recorded all the elements that made up Royke Larson.

As Sandi and Mike cleared away the coffee cups, dessert plates, and beer cans, Royke got to his feet, stretched, then took the two steps that closed the distance between him and Stacy. Standing over her, he extended his hand.

"You'll be leaving in the morning." One of the evening's topics had been her departure, so Royke was not asking a question but merely reiterating a fact. Stacy answered anyway.

"Yes, early."

His long fingers wrapped around her small hand when she placed it in his, sending a tingling electric current up her arm. "Then I'll say good-night, and goodbye."

Expecting him to release her, Stacy blinked in surprise when his fingers tightened slightly. Stacy smiled tremulously. "Good night, Royke. I...I..." Whatever she had been about to say went right out of her mind as Royke bent over her.

"And, Stacy, keep repeating to yourself that there really is very little to fear about flying," he murmured.

"I know that intellectually, but..." Stacy shook her shoulders in a helpless shrug.

A gentle smile curved his lips as he straightened. Still he did not release her hand. "Then you'll have to go to Plan B." The gleam in his eye belied his serious tone.

"And that is?" Stacy prompted him, curious.

"Several double vodka martinis before boarding."

"Early in the morning?" Stacy burst out laughing.

Royke nodded solemnly. "It's called fighting fire with firewater." A grin lent a rakish cast to his features as he released her and stepped back. "Have a safe trip home. I'll be looking forward to reading your article."

Now, hours later, Stacy sat shivering on the small bed, trying to decide if there had been a hidden warning in Royke's parting statement or if he had been merely indicating an interest in how she'd handle the piece on Sandi.

Sighing softly into the darkness, she eased herself onto her back and pulled the covers up to her chin.

Of course he'd been warning her, she thought wearily. No, Royke had been reinforcing his earlier warning about not hurting Sandi.

Sandi and Royke.

Moving her head sharply from side to side, Stacy rejected the idea of any intimacy between the two; Sandi was too obviously in love with Mike. Besides, throughout that long afternoon Stacy had detected nothing but deep respect and sisterly affection in Sandi's demeanor toward Royke.

So that left Royke, suffering from unrequited love for his best friend's wife.

And that left Stacy halfway in love with Royke herself.

Her eyes flew wide with shock and she bolted upright on the bed.

The mere idea of her feeling anything at all for Royke was not only ludicrous but impossible! She did not believe in love!

Stacy shook her head, but she could not dislodge the tormenting voice of her conscience.

Run home, if you must, but don't delude yourself with excuses. Face the fact that you're running away from something, not to something. Royke frightens you simply because he represents a challenge to all your preconceived notions. And in truth, what you fear is yourself more than Royke.

Never had she been so aware of herself as a woman as when she'd been locked in the strength of Royke's arms; and she had felt herself more a woman ever since. Because the feeling made her vulnerable—to all kinds of new and different emotions—it frightened her.

Stacy knew she had to run away.

The inner conflict resolved, she lay back down and drifted off to sleep.

It was the absence of noise that woke Stacy the next morning. An odd silence prevailed inside and out. Thinking it too early for anyone to be up, Stacy scooped her slim watch off the tiny nightstand and glanced at the face, frowning as she noted the time. It wasn't all that early.

Deciding that everyone, even the birds, had overslept, she slipped out of bed and shrugged into her robe before striding down the hall. She went into the kitchen without even bothering to glance out the window.

Sandi was sitting at the table exactly as she had been the day before, her hands curled around a mug of steaming coffee.

"Well, good morning!" Sandi smiled sleepily. "What drove you from the warmth of your bed at this hour?"

"I think it was the quiet," Stacy confessed. "Where is everybody?"

"Mike's been gone since first light, and the kids are still asleep." Sandi smiled wryly. "Have you looked outside?" When Stacy shook her head, Sandi said, "I think you'd better. Unless I miss my guess, you won't be flying anywhere today."

Stacy crossed to the wide kitchen window and drew back the burlap-weave café curtain. She gasped at the sight that met her gaze.

Ice! Everything was coated with ice! The rain of the night before had frozen into a glitteringly beautiful yet treacherous glaze that covered the landscape.

"Oh, no!" Stacy's moan was barely audible, yet Sandi heard it.

"'Fraid so," she murmured. "I didn't even bother waking the kids—school's closed." Sandi lifted her shoulders in a helpless shrug. "You can call the airport, but I'm sure you'll find that all flights are grounded."

Spinning around, Stacy retraced her steps

to the opposite wall and the phone that hung on it. Less than five minutes later she replaced the receiver; Sandi's prediction proved correct.

"They have no idea when they'll get clearance to fly," she said dejectedly. "I was given the option of going to the airport to wait or changing my flight till a later time. I said I'd get back to them."

Dropping into a chair opposite Sandi, she smiled her thanks for the coffee the other woman had poured for her while she was on the phone. Then she sighed.

"I sure don't relish the idea of sitting all day in the airport departure lounge, but I don't know what else to do."

"Stay here," Sandi suggested. "The original plan was for you to stay a few days anyway...so stay. You can always change your reservations for later in the week."

Stay. Stacy savored the enticing word. If she were completely honest with herself, she would admit to wanting to stay, wanting to see Royke again, if only once more.

Why not? What earthly difference could a day or two make?

"All right." The decision made, Stacy grinned at Sandi. "But don't think I'm not going to take advantage of the delay. I'm going to grill you till you feel like a char-broiled hamburger."

"Be my guest," Sandi invited her magnanimously.

Stacy took Sandi up on her offer. Fully expecting to conduct her queries while dodging children, dogs, and Mike, Stacy was pleasantly surprised to see little evidence of them.

The dogs were confined to their backyard pen. Set free for the day, the children occupied themselves in their rooms. And Stacy saw neither hide nor hair of Mike. Curiosity got the best of Stacy when Mike didn't appear at lunchtime.

"Mike still mending fences?" she asked idly, for the second time wondering how one went about mending a fence.

The two oldest children looked at her as if she'd just dropped in from another planet. Sandi smiled wryly.

"No. He's bringing the calves in to shelter." Sandi turned worried eyes to the window. "Weather like this could cause us to lose some,'' she explained. ''Mike's trying to save as many as he can.''

''You mean they could freeze?'' Stacy asked, appalled.

''Or sicken.'' Sandi nodded. ''And with an outfit this small we really can't afford to lose any.

''Before these charming monsters were born I used to help him bring the calves in when necessary,'' Sandi went on. ''Of course, that was also before we had the sheltering pens. Come to that, we still wouldn't have the pens if Royke hadn't loaned us the money.'' She chuckled softly. ''And now Royke's out there helping Mike…again.''

Stacy frowned. ''Doesn't Royke have calves that need looking after?''

''Of course, more than we do,'' Sandi said with a grin. ''One helluva lot more. But Royke also has hired hands to do the looking after.'' Stacy's frown deepened and Sandi held up her hand. ''Let me correct what I'm sure you're thinking. Royke is no absentee rancher. He is very definitely a working rancher. He is also a good neighbor and friend. He pays his help well, and he hires the

best. They know what to do whether he's
there or not.''

Sandi had read Stacy like a book; she had
been wondering if Royke was an absentee
rancher. Coloring with embarrassment, she
nonetheless persisted. ''Is Royke away often?''

''Off and on,'' Sandi replied. ''After
Royke's mother left, his father did become an
absentee rancher. He left the running of the
property to his foreman, Matt Parker, while
he went out to conquer new fields, most of
them oil.'' Sighing, she lifted her shoulders
in a helpless shrug. ''Royke runs himself rag-
ged overseeing all the holdings his father left
him. And Matt Parker still runs the ranch.''

So, Royke is a businessman as well as a
man of the land, Stacy mused as she ate her
grilled cheese sandwich. A many-talented
man. Was he also a dangerous man? she wondered.

Suddenly uncomfortable with her own
thoughts, Stacy avoided them by engaging the
children in conversation.

After lunch the dishes were dispensed with,
young David was put into his bed for a nap,

and the two eldest Cases were dispatched with an order to "clean up your rooms." Then, the interview forgotten, Sandi and Stacy embarked on a "girl talk" session.

Their conversation ranged from clothes to the theater and movies, and every and any other subject that came to either one's mind. As the afternoon wore on, Stacy was mildly shocked at the realization that she was confiding more and more of her inner feelings to Sandi. Often bored or upset by hearing the confidences of her friends, Stacy rarely confided in others. The fact that she'd allowed herself to be so easily drawn out by Sandi was a mark of the closeness developing between them.

To her own amazement, Stacy heard herself pouring out the dissatisfaction she'd been experiencing lately—with her job, with her life, and most amazing of all, with her mother and her mother's off-again, on-again lovers.

"I must be a moral coward," she confessed late in the afternoon. "If I had any guts at all, I'd not only move into my own apartment, but change my job *and* my life-style."

Sandi's smile was maternal. "We're all

creatures of habit, Stacy. We tend to hang on to what we know and what is comfortable." She laughed softly. "Even if what is comfortable makes us uneasy occasionally."

"But I'm twenty-five years old!" Stacy groaned disgustedly. "And still living under my mother's wing, *and* by her wishes."

"And you're convinced you're the only twenty-five-year—"

Whatever Sandi had been about to say was lost in Mike Jr.'s excited cry of interruption.

"Hey, Mom, it's snowing! I'll bet we don't have school tomorrow, either!"

Chapter Seven

Snowing.

Straightening his back slowly, Royke lifted his face to the swirling white flakes. First ice, now snow. Welcome spring!

If it snows long enough and hard enough, she might not be able to leave for several days.

The anticipatory pleasure Royke felt at that thought shocked his rancher's mind. Bad spring weather could be damned costly if not disastrous to a cattle rancher, and here he was, grinning like an idiot. Shaking his head in despair, Royke glanced at Mike with a grimace as the other man walked up to him, massaging stiff shoulder muscles.

"Thanks for your help, Royke," Mike said softly. "I really don't think we'll lose any now." Sweeping his Stetson from his head, Mike raked his fingers through his hair. "Come back with me for supper?"

"No time," Royke said shortly. "I want to check out my own stock before dark." Tilting his head back again, he squinted at the heavy-looking gray sky. "Looks like we're gonna have our work cut out for us tomorrow, too," he said wearily.

"Appears so," Mike agreed, smiling weakly. He waved as Royke started for his four-wheel-drive vehicle.

Royke's drive home over the snow-covered ice was even more harrowing than the trip out had been that morning, and it should have commanded his complete attention. But, though he kept his eyes glued to the road, Royke found his thoughts wandering to the woman he had just denied himself the plea-sure of seeing.

And he wanted to look into Stacy's lovely

face more than he wanted a dry change of clothes and a hot meal!

The big vehicle swerved and Royke, cursing softly, gripped the wheel tightly. Mind your business, cowboy, he advised himself harshly, before you find yourself upside down under a pile of metal! The woman will keep; the weather won't.

Still, before turning his full concentration to the road, Royke promised himself one more kiss from Ms. Stacy Ernshaw.

On the third morning of her visit with Sandi Case, Stacy flung herself out of the bed and flew to the window. Raking the curtain back with trembling fingers, she let a soft "Oh" whisper through her parted lips at the world of white that met her gaze. Not only was the snow piled high everywhere, but it was still coming down in thick white clouds.

With the knowledge that she would not be going anywhere very soon, Stacy had a slow shower before dressing in corduroy jeans, a heavy knit pullover sweater, and her shockingly expensive leather boots. Disdaining makeup as unnecessary, she scraped a brush through her hair, then strolled out of the room whistling softly through her neat white teeth.

This morning Sandi was not in the kitchen, but as soon as she heard Stacy enter the kitchen she called from the laundry room, "Have some juice, Stacy, I'll be with you in a few minutes."

Sipping slowly from the small juice glass, Stacy walked to the doorway into the laundry room.

"Laundry again?" she asked incredulously. "You did three loads yesterday."

"And I've got at least that many today," Sandi drawled. "With this snow I'll more than likely have the same tomorrow."

"What does the snow have to do with it?" Stacy frowned.

"What does the..." Sandi whooped with laughter. "Boy! It's plain to see you aren't around kids much! My adorable little heathens will be in and out all day. And they'll need dry clothes every time they come in." Groaning theatrically, she ran a hand over her gleaming dark hair. "No wonder I'm getting old and gray."

Stacy smiled teasingly. "Poor darling,

youth and beauty gone, and all in the name of love." Arching one eyebrow, she said, "There isn't a gray hair on your head and you know it. And, at the advanced age of thirty-one, you're younger than almost everyone I know."

"Ain't it the truth?" Sandi giggled, sliding an arm around Stacy's waist. "God, I'm glad you got iced—and now snowed—in. Having you here has been wonderful. Even though I get to town about once a week and talk my fool head off on the phone with my friends, I do miss the female companionship of my single days." She winked conspiratorially. "Even if your man happens to be your best friend, as Mike is mine, there are some things you'd say to a woman that you wouldn't dream of saying to any man!"

After breakfast Stacy agreed to go outside with the children to help build a snowman. She went to her room and took her long suede coat from the closet. Shrugging into it as she entered the kitchen, she called, "Ready, kids?"

"You can't romp in the snow in that!"

Sandi screeched. "You'll ruin it, and it must have cost a fortune!"

"Oh, for heaven's sake, the animal it came from probably wore it in the snow. And besides, I have nothing else to wear." Pulling leather gloves over her hands, Stacy headed for the door.

"You stay right where you are," Sandi ordered sharply. "I absolutely forbid you to mess up that gorgeous thing. And those gloves won't do you any good in the snow." Digging into the deep closet just inside the kitchen door, Sandi produced a quilted jacket and a bulky pair of mittens.

"You can wear these," she declared, holding the clothes out to Stacy. "The jacket may be a little big on you, but it will keep you warm."

Outside, the snow was still falling steadily, though not as heavily as when Stacy had wakened. Breathing deeply, she gazed over the property and its assortment of out-buildings. There was the barn with the corral to one side and behind. To the other side of the barn and beyond were several other long, low, shedlike buildings. Stacy hadn't the vaguest idea what they were used for.

In the distance, barely visible behind a low knoll, was the small house that Sandi had told her was the original homestead built by Mike's grandfather. From her discussions with Sandi, Stacy knew the house was now occupied by the two hands employed by Mike: a widower and his son, whom Stacy had yet to meet.

"They keep pretty much to themselves," Sandi had said that first morning when Stacy had trailed behind her to the chicken pens. "Young Jake has a girlfriend living with him. She keeps house and does their cooking for them. Before she moved in they took their meals here."

"Doesn't she ever come up here to visit with you?" Stacy asked, wondering at Sandi's casual attitude to the arrangement.

"Rarely." Sandi's smile had indicated her understanding of Stacy's confusion. "She only moved in late last fall and, as the winter was pretty severe, she didn't venture out too often." Her smile turned soft. "I think she's pregnant."

Shocked, Stacy had exclaimed, "Good grief! And she's all alone most of the time down there! What if something were to happen? An accident or something?"

"I'm as close as the telephone, Stacy." Sandi laughed chidingly.

Now, with the happy squeals of the children ringing in her ears, Stacy stared at the small house feeling admiration and respect. Did she possess the kind of courage and perseverance these women of the West seemed to be endowed with? she wondered. Could she face life out here calmly, stoically, or even, as in Sandi's case, happily?

Stacy knew she could be tough when she was digging out facts for an article. But she also knew she was soft, used to the comforts and luxuries afforded by earning a good salary in a large city. Could she not only exist but thrive in Sandi's world as Sandi had at one time thrived in hers?

Sighing softly, Stacy turned to the children, who were urging her to join their play. She honestly did not know if she had the stuff pioneers were made of, but then, it really didn't matter. The chances were slim to none that she'd ever have to face that particular test.

The hours of the morning spun out, filled with shouts of laughter from the children and Stacy. At periodic intervals they trooped into the house to warm themselves with cups of steaming hot chocolate. On the first trip indoors Sandi silently held a navy blue knit cap out to Stacy. Her devilish grin matching David's, Stacy pulled the cap down over her damp curls and fiery red ears. Their number was depleted on their second dash into the house when David, complaining of cold feet, was whisked out of his snowsuit and into a warm bath by his scolding mother.

At noon they sat down to a lunch of juicy cheeseburgers and cups of rich chicken soup. Mike Jr., Laura, and an unusually animated Stacy regaled Sandi with tales of the morning's adventures. David added little to the chatter as he was half-asleep on his stool.

The moment the lunch clutter had been cleared away, the kids challenged Stacy to a snowball fight. Ashamed to admit to weariness, Stacy stomped her feet back into her boots, shrugged into the quilted jacket, and

went marching after the seemingly tireless
youngsters.

The moment Stacy set foot in the side yard
she was pelted with a loosely packed snowball. Laughing as uninhibitedly as the kids,
she joined in the fray, unmindful of the fact
that her sweater was getting wet because the
buttons on her borrowed jacket had slipped
through the loose holes. Chilled, yet perspir-
ing from the furious activity, she was not disappointed when Sandi opened the back door
to call the kids inside.

"Are you three snow-blind?" Sandi
shouted exasperatedly. "Can't you see the
storm has practically turned into a blizzard?"

Grumbling about never being able to have
any fun, Mike and Laura trudged into the
house while Stacy, actually noticing the wild-
ness of the storm for the first time, stood staring at the whirling white onslaught in awe.
Stacy had witnessed blizzards before, but
never had she stood in the middle of one.

The looming mountains were completely
obscured by the density of the low-hanging
snow clouds. In fact, Stacy could barely make
out the barn.

Suddenly aware of the cold, Stacy shivered. As she turned to follow the children into the house, a dim, moving outline caught her attention. Pausing, she peered through the snow. As the object made its ponderous way into the yard, Stacy began to discern the high front end of a tractor, which was towing a long flatbed wagon. Turning back, she watched its slow progress until it disappeared into the barn. Moments later two men emerged from the barn. Working together, they managed to close and fasten the wide double doors before moving, heads bent, toward her.

Even with their hats pulled low and their jacket collars turned up high the men were recognizable. As they approached her, Mike tossed her a crooked grin.

"Trying to get a tan, Stacy?" he teased, not breaking stride as he made for the door and the welcoming warmth of his family and kitchen.

Stacy opened her mouth to reply, but Royke forestalled her.

"Or are you trying to get pneumonia, Stacy?" Royke came to a stop directly in

front of her, his glance taking in the sparkle
in her eyes, her cold-reddened cheeks, and the
jacket that was hanging open, exposing her to
the elements. "You know," he mused, tugging the heavy gloves from his hands, "for a
smart lady, you aren't very bright." Stuffing
his gloves into the deep pockets of his sheep-
skin-lined coat, Royke brought his hands to
the bottom button of her jacket. His fingers
working swiftly, he slid the buttons into their
loose holes. After fastening the last one, he
grasped the quilted material lightly with his
fingertips and tugged gently, drawing her
closer to him.

"You should go inside." Making no move
to release her, Royke stared intently into her
eyes.

"Yes," Stacy agreed breathlessly, knowing he was right, yet unable to break his hold
on her. Then, more breathlessly still, she
gasped, "No!" as he lowered his head.

"I promised myself this," Royke muttered
an instant before his lips touched hers.

It was not at all like it had been a few days
before in the laundry room. It was not at all
like anything Stacy had ever experienced.

Gently, delicately, but very surely, Royke's mouth covered hers, moving slowly until they fit together perfectly.

With infinite care he pried Stacy's unresisting lips apart, caressing the tender inner skin with the tip of his tongue, then sliding it along the edges of her teeth. Royke continued to move his mouth against hers, waiting for her response.

With all her senses seeming to explode, Stacy withstood the enticement of Royke's maddeningly light touch for as long as she could. Then, a tiny moan of protest clogging her throat, she leaned into the kiss invitingly.

Stacy's moan was echoed by Royke's harsh groan, and then his hands released the material of her jacket to sweep down the front of it, tearing open the buttons he'd fastened moments before. When his own coat was hanging open, too, he slid his arms around her waist and pulled her roughly to his hard, muscled chest. His mouth locked over hers.

Made mindless by the urgency of newly awakened needs, and light-headed from the rush of blood through her veins, Stacy curled her arms around his strong neck and clung.

Unmindful of the freezing cold and the wet snow covering their shoulders, Royke led Stacy into a tropical world of sensuality. Hungrily, as if he could not get enough of her, he deepened the kiss, his tongue searching, probing for all the sweetness she had to offer.

Stacy felt Royke's body harden with need and demand, and her own soften in response. Wanting, *needing,* more of him, she pressed herself closer, even as she felt his arms tighten to crush her to him. At that moment, on fire with desire so compelling it was like being burned alive, Stacy would not have murmured the mildest protest had Royke attempted to lower her to the bed of snow and take possession of her in the howling blizzard.

The very intensity of the emotions raging through her brought about her release. Shuddering in reaction to Royke and her own willingness to surrender completely to him, Stacy whimpered softly. Feeling her tremble, hearing her muted cry, Royke lifted his head and stepped back.

"I must be out of my mind," he growled. "You're freezing! If I don't get you inside soon, you really will come down with pneumonia!'' Clasping her to his side with one arm, he led her out of the snow and back to sanity.

Mike and Sandi were alone in the kitchen.

"What in the world were you two doing out there all this time?" Sandi asked, frowning at their snow-covered heads and shoulders.

"Admiring the sunset," Royke drawled, shedding his jacket.

Feeling a flush crawl up her throat, Stacy busied herself with removing her own wet clothes and avoiding Sandi's shrewd eyes.

"Admiring the sunset, indeed!" Sandi mumbled, setting out cups, then filling them with coffee. "I've heard that heavy atmospheric pressure does affect some people, but I thought the effect was on the sinuses, not the mind!" Shaking her head in despair, she carried the cups to the table. "Come, drink this," she ordered. "You need something to chase the chill. You could both do with a bowl of hot soup, too."

"I could do with a helluva lot more than a bowl of soup." Royke grinned, dropping into

the chair beside Stacy. "I haven't eaten since
four-thirty this morning."

"The hamburgers are under the broiler,"
Sandi said, sliding a large bowl of soup in
front of him. "Stacy, do you want some
soup?"

"Uh-uh." Stacy shook her head, wrapping
her numb fingers around the warm cup. "This
is fine."

Keeping her mind off what had transpired
between her and Royke proved darned near
impossible for Stacy while he was sitting
right beside her at the table. And his attitude
of cool unconcern didn't help much, either!

Was Royke so used to making love to
women he barely knew that he could dismiss
it as of little importance? Had he been amus-
ing himself after a particularly frustrating
morning? For from the men's conversation,
Stacy gathered that the morning had been
both frustrating and grueling. Or, she wondered miserably, had Royke used her as a
substitute for the woman he really wanted to
kiss?

Tormenting herself by looking for reasons
for Royke's sudden ardor, Stacy was only

dimly aware of the conversation going on around her. The men were telling Sandi of the job they'd had spreading feed for the cattle, and how they'd have to start all over again the next morning, but it wasn't until a chair was scraped back from the table that Stacy's reverie ended.

"I'm going to go soak my frozen feet in a hot tub," Mike declared. "How about you, Royke?"

Slicing a glance at Stacy, Royke slowly shook his head. "Stacy's still shivering. I'll wait till she's had a bath or a shower."

"No!" Stacy protested. "You go ahead. I'm fine, really," she insisted when he frowned. "I'm going to have another cup of coffee, and then help Sandi clean up."

"Well..."

"Really, I'm okay," she urged him when he appeared to weaken. "Call me when you're finished."

In truth Stacy was still shivering, but the chills shaking her slender frame were caused more by her thoughts than by her damp clothing. As she was obviously not going to budge,

Royke, with a small smile of gratitude, stood up stiffly and followed Mike out of the room.

"What *were* you two doing out there all that time?" Sandi asked softly the minute the men were out of hearing range.

"Just…ah…watching it snow," Stacy lied.

"Sure. And I believe that the way I believe that babies come out of pea pods!" Laughing at the flame of color firing Stacy's cheeks, Sandi began clearing the table.

Stacy was drying the last soup bowl when Royke's call reverberated through the entire house.

"It's all yours, Stace."

Stace. The sound of her shortened name echoing in her mind, Stacy went to her room to get her robe. With a delicious tingle dancing down her back, she hurried into the bathroom. *Stace.* Nobody had ever called her that before. Stacy decided she liked it.

Standing inside the bathroom, Stacy drew a deep breath. Royke's scent lingered on the steamy air, filling her mind with a memory of how very close to him she'd been a short time ago. Sighing softly, longingly, she closed the drain and turned on the hot-water tap. By the

time the tub was filled to within a few inches
of the rim, Stacy had peeled off her damp
jeans and sweater. Slipping down into the hot
water, she rested her head on the edge of the
tub and promptly fell into a doze.

The coolness of the air in the room and the
water lapping gently around her body woke
Stacy with a start. Beginning to shiver all
over again, she washed quickly and stepped
out of the tub to wrap herself in a large towel.

After dressing in the gold suede skirt she'd
traveled in and a contrasting sweater in a rich
shade of chocolate brown, Stacy slid her feet
into beige satin slippers, applied a light coat-
ing of makeup to her glowing face, then gave
her curls a vigorous brushing. Standing back
from the mirror, she ran a critical glance over
her reflection. Not bad, she thought whimsi-
cally. You'll never intimidate a high-fashion
model but you'll do in a pinch.

The first thing that struck Stacy as she left
her room was the quiet that had descended on
the house. When she'd entered the bathroom
the kids had been playing a noisy board game
in the living room, most of the noise created

by David who was too young to understand
the game in the first place.

Now, the tranquillity of the atmosphere
washed over Stacy like a balm. She was tired
from all the unaccustomed physical activity,
and the silence was restful. But where had
everybody disappeared to? she wondered.

Walking through the archway into the living room, Stacy ran her gaze over the area,
coming to a stop on the two men at the desk
in the front corner, near the wide window.

Mike was sitting at the desk speaking quietly. Standing beside him, Royke nodded his
understanding of whatever Mike was explaining. There were no signs of the children or
Sandi.

Almost as if he'd sensed her presence,
Royke lifted his head and tilted it to watch
Stacy as she crossed the room to sit on the
couch.

"The kids are all taking naps," he informed her before she had a chance to ask.
"And Sandi's attacking a pile of mending."
Royke's slow smile jolted through Stacy like
an earthquake. "I assured her you'd be able
to amuse yourself for a few hours." Although

it wasn't a question, Royke lifted one dark brow. At Stacy's calm nod, he added tauntingly, "I also assured her that you'd be more than willing to make a fresh pot of coffee for me and Mike if we wanted it—" now his smile was the devil's own "—and we do." Royke's hesitation was slight but obvious. "Can you handle that? The coffee, I mean?"

At that instant Stacy learned that it was possible to want to slap a person and long to kiss him at one and the same time. Choosing prudence over stupidity, Stacy merely smiled and rose, smoothing the suede with her suddenly damp palms before making a regal exit.

Actually, Stacy made very good coffee and she knew it. After preparing the electric pot, she plugged it into a socket above the countertop, and walked to the window to look at the snow while she waited for the coffee to perk.

She never heard Royke as he walked into the room to stand behind her. When he spoke she stiffened with shock, even though his voice was pitched low.

"Beautiful."

Her gaze riveted to the window, Stacy was

totally unaware that Royke's eyes rested on her profile and not on the snow-covered world beyond the glass.

"Yes," she murmured innocently.

"And exciting," Royke added very softly.

Exciting? Well, perhaps...though she would not have applied that particular adjective to the scene outside.

"Hmm," she murmured absently, too caught in the scent of him, the warmth radiating from his body, to be interested in the snow. For now, Stacy was content simply to have Royke near and to hear the low, soothing sound of his voice.

"Sandi tells me you're unhappy." Royke's tone dropped even lower. "With your job, and your home life...in fact with your entire life-style."

Stacy's contentment was instantly shattered. Sandi had *told* him? Everything? The sense of betrayal was crushing. Closing her eyes, Stacy fought to contain the hot tears that stung behind her lids. For the first time in years Stacy had felt safe enough with a friend to confide in her; and her trusted friend had broken that trust. Stacy spun around to confront Royke.

"Sandi had no right to tell you anything about me!" she protested harshly. "No right to repeat what I told her in con—"

"She's concerned about you," Royke said, slicing through her objection every bit as harshly. "For some reason she feels protective of you. Sandi was merely using me as a sounding board. She wants to help you and doesn't know how."

"That's no excuse for breaking a confi—"

"I do." Royke again cut her off.

Confusion tempered her anger. Stacy stared at him blankly.

"What?"

"I do know how to help you," he said quietly.

Suddenly wary, Stacy examined his face for telltale signs of ridicule, and found none. Royke's expression was not only serious, it was coolly austere. Made curious in spite of herself, Stacy had to ask the obvious.

"How?"

"I know you're a journalist," Royke said. "But are you also a chronicler?"

A chronicler? What in the... "What are you talking about?" she demanded impatiently.

"It's important for me to know if you can put facts together in chronological order," Royke explained.

"Well, of course I can!" she snapped. "But what does that have to do with anything?"

"It has everything to do with the proposition I have for you," Royke responded calmly.

Chapter Eight

Proposition? Royke had a proposition for her?

"Explain your proposition, *please*," she challenged him haughtily.

Stacy's icy tone was met by a soft chuckle from Royke. "It's nothing illegal or immoral," he assured her, unsuccessfully attempting to control the twitch of amusement tugging at the corners of his lips. "What I'm offering is a proposal of marriage." Ignoring her shocked gasp, he went on. "A marriage of convenience, if you will."

"I think you're absolutely crazy!" Shaking

with anger and embarrassment, Stacy moved
to escape his taunting presence only to find
her way blocked by his large body. Clenching
her teeth, she gritted out, "Fun-and-games
time is over. Please let me pass."

"No." Bracing his hands against the window frame on either side of her, Royke effectively caged her in. "I'm not playing
games, Stacy. You will stay where you are
until I've explained."

"Oh, I wish you would, Mr. Larson,"
Stacy purred icily. "I'm waiting with bated
breath."

Though Royke's eyes narrowed, his expression remained placid. "Okay, here's the
deal. I have a pile of journals, diaries, note-
books and the like that were kept by my ancestors, beginning with the first Larson that
set foot in Montana. I want them sorted and
compiled into a family chronicle." Royke
paused, then went on more quickly. "I've
been told the job would entail a massive
amount of work. If you agree to
my...bargain, that would be your work. In
exchange, I'm offering you not only the use
of my study, but the entire house—" again

there was a slight, telling pause "—and my name as well."

Stacy's eyes widened as her mouth dropped open. Unable to believe she'd heard him correctly, she stared at him in amazement until he growled, "Well?"

"Why don't you simply hire someone to do the work?" she asked, shaking her head in bewilderment.

"Because that's where my side of the convenience comes in." Positive he had her full attention now, Royke let his arms drop to his sides and straightened.

"I've decided it is time I married," he went on coolly. "I need a son to leave the property to, and I'm not getting any younger." His attitude was now chillingly withdrawn. After a moment Royke raised a quizzical brow. "Are you interested?"

"You *are* crazy!" Stacy whispered, fighting a shudder of revulsion. Never in her life had Stacy heard such a cold-blooded, emotionless proposal.

"Hardly," Royke drawled. "Actually, I think I've worked everything out rather intelligently."

Stung by his offhand assurance, Stacy attacked him. "Then I wish you'd explain your
reasoning to me, because I sure as hell can't
decipher it!" Not for her weight in gold could
Stacy figure out why she continued to listen
to him; every word he uttered was pure lu-
nacy!

Although Royke tensed, his tone remained
unruffled. "That's because you're thinking
emotionally not logically." His lips curved
sardonically. "You are obviously considering
the state of marriage from a romantic position, whereas I am looking at it from a more
realistic angle."

"What realistic angle?" Stacy inserted
forcefully.

"You're beautiful," Royke said, thoroughly confusing her with his bland assertion.
"And I am not, shall we say, unattractive?"

"You know darned well you're not!"
Stacy snorted, earning a grin from Royke for
her interruption.

"We're both reasonably bright individu-
als," he continued dryly. "The odds are, we
would produce an equally attractive, intelligent child together." Before Stacy could as

much as gasp, Royke added, "And we know the physical chemistry works between us. Don't we?"

Stacy had a flashing image of the intensity of the kiss they'd shared in the yard. Oh, yes, she had to give him that! The chemistry sure did work! But enough for marriage? The man was insane! Moistening her parched lips with the tip of her tongue, Stacy felt a tingle of awareness as Royke's eyes followed the wet trail. Shaking her head, she started to edge around him.

"This conversation is ridiculous," she declared firmly, as much to convince him as herself. "I wouldn't dream..."

"Think about it," Royke insisted, halting her movement by curling long fingers around her wrist.

"But—" she began, only to be silenced again.

"Stacy! I only asked you to think about it carefully, rationally." Drawing a deep breath, Royke said quietly, "It's an honorable proposal. We would lose nothing by joining forces...we could only gain. Will you at least think about it?"

Quite positive that Royke wouldn't hesitate to keep her trapped in the kitchen all night waiting for her to agree, she nodded her head sharply once. "All right, Royke, I'll think about it." As he started to smile, she snapped, "But I know now what my decision will be."

Stepping back, Royke waved his hand to indicate that she was free to go. "Remember, Stacy," he softly cautioned her as she forced herself to walk slowly to the counter and the long-since-finished coffee. "Think unemotionally and logically."

Thoroughly rattled, Stacy tossed her head as she reached for the cups in the cabinet above the sink. Ordering her trembling hand to be still, she poured the dark brew into three cups, then asked tersely, "Exactly how long would you like me to consider this ridiculous offer?"

Strolling up to her, Royke plucked two cups from her nerveless fingers. "There's nothing ridiculous about my proposal, and you know it." Turning toward the living room, he tossed over his shoulder, "Take as long as you like. But keep in mind that the planes won't be grounded for long."

Sandi found Stacy some twenty minutes later, staring into the coffee she'd poured for herself but hadn't touched.

"What are you doing out here alone?" she wondered aloud.

"Thinking," Stacy replied distractedly. Thinking about a man prepared to marry a woman he did not love because he could not have the woman he did.

"Well, I'm afraid I must intrude on your reverie," Sandi said with a grin. "Would you believe those two wranglers are hungry again?"

I believe one of them is very hungry. Smiling despite the sudden tightness in her chest, Stacy placed her cold coffee on the countertop.

"So, what have we got for them?" she inquired with forced lightness.

It was while they all wolfed down salami sandwiches and mugs of beer that Stacy received her second jolt of the day. It came from Mike.

"You're not even thinking of going home, Royke."

"No," Royke agreed, squashing Stacy's

hopes. "I doubt I'd get out of the yard with the truck. I'll wait till morning, then borrow a horse."

Stacy bemoaned her rotten luck. It had been bad enough before, when all she'd had to worry about was the physical pull between them, but now, knowing she could have him, all of him, for the asking, she could hardly stand it.

Damned if she wasn't tempted to accept his stupid offer!

The thought plagued Stacy throughout the rest of the afternoon and evening, and she heaved a silent sigh of relief when the group broke up soon after nine-thirty.

Yawning and stretching, Mike got to his feet and announced, "I don't know about the rest of you, but I'm bushed." Rubbing a palm over his hair, he grimaced. "And it's going to be a long day tomorrow."

"Damned straight." Royke sighed. "I'm for the sack, too." Ambling toward the hallway and the cot that had been set up for him in with the boys, he muttered, "I'll see you early, Mike. G'night, Sandi, Stacy."

After helping Sandi to straighten up the living room, Stacy was only too happy to seek her own bed; she had some heavy thinking to do.

A small fire in her stomach woke Stacy the next morning. Absently rubbing her midriff, she swung her legs over the side of the bed and sat up. With full wakefulness came the realization that she hadn't felt the burning pain since her arrival at the ranch.

"Must have been the salami and beer," she muttered, pulling her nightgown over her head.

Dressing in jeans and her last clean sweater, Stacy smiled in self-derision. The night had been long and restless, and she knew full well that the fire inside her stomach was caused by worry, and not what she'd eaten.

Why she had wasted even one minute, let alone over half the night, deliberating on Royke's rather insulting proposal was beyond her. And the worst part was that she had actually caught herself weakening to his argument in the wee hours of the morning!

Was insanity contagious?

Grimacing at her image in the mirror, Stacy gave up on trying to bring some order to her chestnut curls and tossed the brush onto the dresser.

Rummaging in her suitcase, she located the bottle of antacid tablets, and popping two into her mouth, strolled to the window to draw back the drapes. Bright sunlight slanted off the sparkling snow. She stepped back, thinking that with any luck at all the planes would be flying again.

She didn't want to go home. Stacy readily admitted that—at least to herself. And she did not have to go home. To remain, all she had to do was to accept Royke's offer of escape.

Insanity!

Stacy pulled open the bedroom door and strode into the hall. It was out of the question, she told herself. Pinch-hitting for another woman would eventually destroy her. Better and safer to follow through with the plans she'd formed during the endless night.

Of course, the first order of business after returning home was to write up the article on Sandi Case, professional homemaker. Then she'd set the gears in motion to change her life, beginning with the acquisition of her own apartment, and ending with a complete change of her present life-style, from friends to employment.

It would not be easy, Stacy knew that. Change was often hard to cope with. Her life until now had been well-ordered and simple. Rearranging everything would be unsettling for her. Then, too, there would be the inevitable arguments with her mother.

When Stacy entered the kitchen, Sandi was busy coaxing the children to finish their breakfast. A warm smile lit her face when she saw Stacy.

"Good morning. Would you mind helping yourself?" she asked, attempting to insert a spoonful of cereal between David's compressed lips. "There's hot oatmeal in the pot, and bacon and sweet rolls warming in the oven. The coffee's fresh."

"'Morning, kids," Stacy greeted them, walking to the stove. "It's a beautiful morning."

"Indeed!" Sandi agreed. "C'mon, David! Mommy hasn't got all day, you know."

"Hate omeal," David mumbled through

tightly clenched teeth. "I want to play in the snow."

Raising her eyes to the ceiling, Sandi gave up the struggle. "Oh, all right! But you just stay put until I've cleaned you up, young man."

The domestic scene, so commonplace for Sandi, was an enlightenment for Stacy. Being an only child, she had never witnessed the interplay of a larger family. Surprisingly, she found herself enjoying it immensely. At the same time she couldn't deny the twinge of envy she felt for Sandi.

While helping the wriggling children into their heavy outdoor clothing, Stacy compared the richness of Sandi's life with the dullness of her own.

Strange, she mused later, after the kids ran whooping out the door, she had set out on this assignment feeling pity for Sandi. Now, less than a week after leaving Philadelphia, Stacy found herself envying the other woman.

Stacy smiled gently at the soft sound of Sandi humming as she loaded the washer in the laundry room. You could have it, too, an insidious voice tempted from deep inside her consciousness. The safe harbor of home and children and husband could all be yours simply by saying yes. Say it! Take what you want and run with it!

Stacy jumped up and walked to the window. It was the wrong thing to do. Seeing the children at play, hearing their laughter ringing in the sharp, clear air, reinforced the urgings of her inner self.

I don't want to go back! The silent cry was a physical thing, shuddering through her entire being.

Say yes! Royke is offering you freedom, and himself. Don't be a fool! Grab it, and him!

Closing her eyes, Stacy actually swayed from the effect of the battle raging within.

I can't! He is not emotionally free! If he were, there might be a chance, a slim chance to make a go of an arranged marriage. But he isn't...he isn't.

Spinning away from the window, she strode to the wall phone.

Stacy was replacing the receiver when Sandi came into the kitchen several minutes later.

"I thought I heard you talking to some-one," Sandi said. "The airport?" she guessed.

"Yes. I have reservations on a flight east late this afternoon." Stacy smiled ruefully. "That is, if I can get to the airport."

"You really must go?" Sandi asked flatly.

"I really must."

"Then you'll get to the airport."

Then Sandi changed the subject, as if try-ing to put off the reality of Stacy's departure for as long as possible.

The hours slipped by until, knowing she could no longer procrastinate, Stacy went to her room to pack. She had barely begun when she heard the phone ring. A few moments later Sandi came to stand in the doorway, a slip of paper in her hand.

"I've just taken a cablegram for you over the phone." Her expression compassionate, she held out the paper, turning away as soon as Stacy took it.

Stacy glanced over the message quickly, then reread it more carefully.

CONGRATULATIONS IN ORDER. JAMES AND I MARRIED THIS MORNING. WE'LL

CELEBRATE WHEN WE GET HOME.

MOTHER

Well, that tears it, Stacy thought tiredly. Forgetting the necessity of packing, she sank onto the bed. Now there was no way she could back out of her hastily formed plans, at least in regard to moving into her own apartment. Nothing would induce her to live with her mother and her new husband.

It wasn't that Stacy didn't like James; she did. But a sixth sense warned her that with a new husband around, her mother would redouble her efforts to find Stacy a matc of her own.

Stacy was staring at the floor when a light tap on the open door broke her dismal reverie. Expecting to see Sandi, she forced a smile to her lips. Her smile wavered when her gaze encountered Royke's steady regard. Without asking permission, he stepped into the room and gently closed the door behind him.

"Sandi tells me you're leaving," he said emotionlessly.

"Yes."

"So your answer is no." A wistful smile touched his lips. "You're going to turn your back on the perfect solution to your problems." A frown drew his brows together. "Why, I wonder?"

Feeling somehow trapped by his probing gaze, Stacy jerked to her feet and walked to the window. "It couldn't work, Royke!" Sighing, she turned to face him. "I've seen too many people rush into marriage only to have it fail when the glow of newness wears off. We don't even know if we like each other! How could we possibly hope to make it work when—"

"I'll tell you how," Royke interrupted softly. "We can make it work because we'll both know exactly what we're contracting for from the beginning. There'll be no 'love glow' to wear off or, for that matter, even an overriding need to share a marriage bed—although we would. As two rational, intelligent adults, we could make it work simply because there wouldn't be the disappointment of unfulfilled expectations."

When he finished speaking, Royke stood still, watching her, waiting. Holding his gaze with difficulty, Stacy fought against the leaden sensation in her middle. She did consider herself a rational, intelligent adult. So then, why was she feeling insulted?

Drawing a shaky breath, she opened her mouth to speak, then closed it again. She was going to say no. She knew she was going to say no. Get on with it, she ordered.

"Well?" Royke's tone was still neutral, his voice still soft. It was obvious that he would not belabor the point. "Yes or no?"

"Yes."

It was hard to tell which one of them was more surprised. Royke at least had the grace not to look triumphant. Stacy merely looked stunned.

Although she knew the piece of paper she clutched in her hand had been a factor in her decision, she also knew it had been the smallest factor. In the final analysis, she had determined to accept whatever he offered her, as long as it included him.

There was an awkward moment of tension, then Royke walked to her slowly. His movement easy, natural, he extended his hand. When Stacy placed her hand in his he curled his long fingers around it and squeezed gently.

"I don't think you'll be sorry," he murmured.

I'm sorry already, Stacy thought, beginning to feel the enormity of the commitment she'd made. As if sensing her apprehension, Royke became briskly businesslike.

"Okay. I have an idea." Releasing her hand, he turned to run a quick glance over her suitcase and clothes, which were lying on the bed. "I suggest we elope."

"Elope!" Stacy cried. "But...but that's ridic—"

"Not at all," he cut her off smoothly. "In fact, it's perfect for our purpose. An extended engagement, or even a short one, would be ridiculous in this case. You're expected back in Philadelphia, right?"

Stacy nodded. She was beyond speech.

"Right." A small smile tugged at the corners of his lips. "Isn't there some old saying about everybody loving lovers?" Royke didn't wait for an answer. "Well, then, what better reason for you to chuck everything than

love? You can say it was love at first sight
and we couldn't wait.''

The irony of his reasoning was almost too
much for Stacy. Had she suddenly lost what
remained of her sanity? She could not go
through with this farce!

But, of course, she did.

It was not until Stacy was standing in the
center of a very expensive hotel room that the
events of the preceding hours caught up with
her. If nothing else, she had learned one
thing: when Royke Larson decided on a
course of action, bystanders need only step
back and watch his smoke!

Royke had pulled off their elopement—escape?—with remarkable ease. Telling her to
finish packing, he went into the kitchen to
inform Sandi and Mike of his intention to
drive Stacy to the airport, which in fact he
did. But instead of boarding a plane for Philadelphia, they took a flight to Las Vegas.

The trip was tiring but uneventful. Still
moving like a precision timepiece, Royke had
shepherded Stacy directly to a small chapel
amidst many other small chapels. There, wit-

nessed by hired strangers, Stacy became
Royke's wife. The ceremony was brief, un-
emotional, and unreal.

Unreal.

Stacy's pensive gaze roamed the opulent
room. The whole thing was unreal! The room
looked as if it had been decorated especially
for an Eastern potentate. Gulping down a rising bubble of hysteria, she questioned her
own sanity.

More than his cold, emotionless proposal,
more even than the swiftness with which he'd
accomplished his goal, this room, with its
gaudy trappings, told Stacy exactly how
Royke felt about her. This was not the type
of room a man brought his bride to. This was
the sort of place a rich rancher, off the range
after a long winter, brought a bought-and-
paid-for bed partner.

What in the world had she let herself in
for? she thought wildly. Why had she agreed
to this craziness? Royke didn't want her.
Royke wanted Sandi! Stacy stiffened in an
attempt to contain the shudder that went
through her. She was nothing more than a

stand-in, a convenient substitute for the woman he really loved.

An image of that woman rose in Stacy's mind, her face glowing with laughter. The sad thing was that Stacy could not hate Sandi, or even feel jealous of her. During her brief visit at the Case ranch, she had come to love Sandi.

Biting her lip, Stacy steeled herself to face the coming hours as she heard the door close softly behind the bellboy. The first words Royke spoke to her relieved her on one point at least.

"I'm sorry about the room, Stacy. It was the only one the hotel had available."

Turning to face him, Stacy shrugged her shoulders lightly. "It is a bit much." Encountering his look of concern, she forced a tremulous smile. "I must admit it's different."

"Too different." Royke didn't return the smile. "It's no more than a damned playpen." Without taking his eyes from hers he indicated the room's lush decor with the sweep of his arm. "Hardly the proper setting for a wedding night."

Royke's last observation sent a shiver of apprehension through Stacy. The tension beginning to simmer between them seemed to be tying her nerve endings into tiny little knots. She tore her gaze from his and caught sight of a bottle of champagne half-buried in ice in a silver bucket.

Royke's gaze followed hers. "We might as well drink it," he drawled wryly, sauntering to the table that held the silver bucket. "It's on the house."

On the point of declining, Stacy thought of the enormous circular bed behind her. Maybe a glass or two, or four, was what she needed to get her through the next few hours, she decided, inching away from the bed.

Royke demonstrated one talent as he opened the bottle expertly with a muffled pop. Watching him pour the golden wine into the fragile glasses, Stacy caught herself wondering what other talents he might possess.

"To a mutually satisfying relationship," he toasted, tapping his glass to hers. "And to my levelheaded bride."

Hurt more than she would have believed possible by Royke's less-than-inspiring accolade, Stacy raised the glass to her lips and emptied it quickly. Though Royke raised his brows in question, he made no comment as he refilled her glass.

As she had had nothing to eat since lunchtime, the wine went straight to Stacy's head. Cautioning herself against making a complete fool of herself, she sipped the cool wine more slowly while guardedly watching the way Royke's lips were beginning to twitch with inner amusement.

"I do believe you're nervous, Mrs. Larson," he teased.

"I...I've..." Stacy paused to moisten lips already wet with wine. "I've never been married before," she finally managed to sputter.

Placing his half-full glass on the table, he walked to her slowly. Her eyes glued to his looming figure, Stacy gulped down the last of her wine.

"Neither have I," he said softly, taking the glass from her cold fingers. "We'll have to learn how to do it together."

It was the "it" that bothered her, Stacy thought, gazing up at him. The "it" she had no previous knowledge or experience of. At that moment Stacy wondered with a sinking feeling if Royke believed she was experienced in the art of *it!*

Obviously Royke did consider her experienced, for he clasped her hand and drew her to the bed with a murmured, "Come, Stacy."

Releasing her hand, he calmly began to undress, arching a brow at her when she didn't move. In all truth, Stacy couldn't move. Unable to tear her eyes from his body, she watched, breathless, as first his jacket, then his shirt, and finally his pants were dropped carelessly to the floor. Beginning to frown at her lack of action, Royke removed his shoes and socks, then hooked his thumbs into the waistband of his briefs. Stacy's eyes widened in wonder as the briefs were cast aside and Royke stood before her in all his male glory.

Royke was the first man Stacy had ever seen completely unclothed. In appreciation of his male beauty she allowed her gaze the pleasure of drifting over his magnificent form. As her gaze lifted, it tangled with the desire clouding his and a shudder tore through her entire body.

"Now it's my turn," he whispered

hoarsely. "Undress for me, Stacy." When still she didn't move, he raised his hands to the buttons on the one and only dress she had packed for her trip west. As the first button slipped through the hole in the soft wool material, Stacy attempted to step back. "No!" Royke's voice was now rough with need. "Let me do it."

Her heart pounding with a mixture of fear and anticipation, Stacy stood trembling while Royke slowly, tenderly, removed every stitch of clothing she was wearing.

"You're very beautiful," he murmured, leaning back to view her entirely. "More beautiful even than..." His voice was muffled as he buried his lips in the curve of her neck.

Had he been about to say more beautiful than Sandi? Stacy wondered sickly as she felt herself being lowered to the bed. The very real possibility that she was right froze the heat of desire that was beginning to cloud her mind.

An earlier thought drifted into her mind, making her cold and unresponsive to Royke's ardor.

She was nothing more than a stand-in, a convenient substitute for the woman he really wanted and loved.

Chapter Nine

"I'm sorry."

Lying on her back inches from Royke's body, Stacy closed her eyes against the tears that suddenly blurred her vision. The consummation of their marriage had been a fiasco, and the fault lay entirely with her.

Royke's approach had been gentle, and even in her innocence Stacy knew it was expert. Though her body had ached to respond, her mind, holding a picture of a black-haired, laughing woman, had refused to allow her to surrender. And so the pain of initiation had been intensified and, crying out, Stacy had tried to draw away by pressing herself into the mattress. Royke had been unable to stop himself although he had murmured his regret. Now she saw him dimly through her tears as he propped himself up to look into her face.

"You have nothing to be sorry for." Royke drew in a deep breath, then let it out slowly in a long sigh. "I should be the one to apologize. I hurt you, and I'm sorry for that." Moving away from her, he rolled off the bed and began pacing the room.

"But, dammit, Stacy!" Royke came to a stop at the curved foot of the bed. "Why didn't you tell me there had been no other men?"

The annoyance in his tone dried the tears in her eyes. Jerking upright, she glared at him. "Why did you assume there had been?" she demanded angrily.

"Well, you'll have to admit that twenty-five-year-old virgins are not so numerous a man is in danger of tripping over them," Royke drawled sardonically. "And with you being so very liberated and all that, I naturally thought…"

"You thought wrong!" Stacy cut in heatedly.

"A fact, my dear, of which I am now shamefully aware," he shot back. Swinging away again, he prowled around the room like a newly confined animal, sublimely unselfconscious of his nakedness. When he turned to her again all trace of annoyance was gone from his face.

"Look, Stacy, this is getting us nowhere." He circled the bed, then sat on the curved side closest to her. "The next time there will be no pain," he promised. Reaching out his hand, he stroked her cheek with his fingertips. There was no way he could miss her attempt to draw back. "I won't pressure you, Stacy. When you feel you are ready, all you have to do is come to my room."

Come to his... Stacy glanced around the room in confusion.

"I mean, after we get home." He smiled. "We'll have to share this bed while we're here."

"How long were you planning to stay here in Vegas?"

"Well, at least overnight." His lips

twitched with amusement. "I haven't been here in quite a while," he went on. "If you have no objections, I'd like to play a little blackjack." He paused, grinning now. "Seeing as how I'm not likely to be playing at anything else."

Talk about unconscious luck!
Staring bleakly at the steadily mounting pile of chips on the table in front of him, Royke tapped the surface lightly to indicate his desire for a hit on top of the king smirking up at him. The dealer slipped a card from the shoe—an ace—blackjack again!

All of a sudden he was the most popular man in that section of the large room... popular with the ladies, at least! Smiling wryly at the gushing young woman standing behind his left shoulder, Royke placed his bet and watched the action of the game unfolding with disinterest.

The only woman he cared to have in his cheering section was nowhere in sight. When last he'd seen her, Stacy was methodically feeding tokens into a voracious dollar machine, the expression on her face one of detached boredom.

A squeal from behind him alerted Royke to the fact that the play was complete; he'd won again! Well, he mused wryly, so much for the theory that a man and his gold are soon parted.

Motioning to the dealer that he was out of the play, Royke collected his chips and stood up, bumping into the gushing young woman in the process.

"Pardon me," he murmured, even though he was fully aware that she'd been crowding him.

"No, please, excuse me!" Sea green eyes stared up at him beguilingly. "It was my fault, really!"

I know. Royke refrained from uttering the obvious. The woman moved with him as he inched through the crowd, away from the table. The corners of his lips tilting in dry amusement, Royke slanted a sideways glance at her; she was beautiful in a professional sort of way.

Where the hell was Stacy, anyway?

Royke glanced at the woman again. "May I buy you a drink with some of this easy money?" he asked, sure of the answer before the woman revealed perfect white teeth in a brilliant smile.

"I'd like that. Yes, thank you."

What you'd really like, honey, is to get those beautifully manicured fingers on this pile of greenbacks, Royke thought wearily, pocketing the bills the cashier counted out for him.

"Well, then, shall we park ourselves in the nearest lounge?"

Once they were seated, Royke nursed his beer as the woman sipped daintily at her champagne cocktail. She was chattering away blithely, imparting what Royke knew was a fictitious life history. As he wasn't listening anyway, Royke couldn't have cared less.

Smiling, nodding, inserting a comment now and then, Royke tuned out the woman's voice and mentally replaced the events that had ensued since he'd placed his ring on Stacy's slim finger.

What an absolute mess he'd made of it! Calling himself all kinds of a fool, Royke cringed inwardly at the recurring memory of Stacy pressing herself into the mattress in an attempt to get away from him.

Lord! The one woman in this world he longed to cherish, and he had hurt her! But how could he have possibly known?

Shifting uncomfortably in the well-padded chair, he smiled encouragingly at the woman and cursed himself and the feeling of urgency that had driven him to act so very precipitately. What had come over him? Had he really wanted her badly enough to rush her headlong into marriage?

Yes, he had, Royke admitted. And still did, come to that! Royke Larson was in love with his wife—the wife he had married for convenience! It was really very funny. So why wasn't he laughing?

"Mister?"

Squashing a desire to snap angrily at the woman, Royke arched a brow quizzically. "Hmm?"

"Does that lady belong to you?" His companion pointed one long-nailed finger at a spot behind him.

Twisting his torso, Royke looked over his shoulder to encounter Stacy's blue eyes regarding him coolly. Damn, the least she could do was to appear upset at finding him with another woman! Suddenly angry at her, at himself, at the whole frustrating situation, he replied too smoothly, "She does." Baring his teeth in a feral smile, he added, "At least legally."

Royke stood and pulled a chair out for his wife. "Sit down and join the party, Stacy. We're celebrating my luck at the table."

"Thank you, I will." Slipping gracefully into the chair, she favored him with a cool smile. "It's too bad the young lady has to leave now."

"Well, *pardon* me!" the other woman snapped, flouncing away.

"Was that nice?" Royke chided, pleased at the ease with which she'd routed the woman.

"Necessary." Stacy smiled sardonically. "I felt duty-bound to protect your newfound wealth."

"How very wifelike." Hating his sarcastic tone, yet unable to stop himself, he added, "Would you like me to hand the money over to you for safekeeping?"

If he'd thought he would get a rise out of her, he was mistaken. With a look of disgust she turned her head to glance around the dimly lit room.

Pack it in, Larson, Royke advised himself tiredly. She isn't going to respond in any way. They'd been at the hotel now for three days. During that time, his ego and pride smarting from his inability to arouse her on their wedding night, he'd tossed verbal barbs at her at every opportunity; his sarcasm had failed to arouse her, either.

Actually, Royke had seen very little of Stacy the last three days, as she had confined herself to their room, except for meals, for the first two of those days. Using her notes, her tape recorder, and a typewriter borrowed from the hotel, she had completed the assigned article on Sandi Case. She had mailed it that morning, after Royke had read it carefully and given his nod of approval.

It was after they'd eaten lunch that she'd finally condescended to accompany him into the casino, where she promptly deserted him the minute he sat down at the table. Royke had placed a chip on the table to hold his seat and followed her. It was not until after she'd purchased a roll of dollar tokens and began feeding them listlessly into a machine that he made his way back to the table.

Now, watching her over the rim of his glass as he drank his beer slowly, Royke sighed in regret for his hasty action. If he had not hurried her into marriage, would she have come to him willingly in time? And then, instead of reluctantly sharing a bed, would they spend the entire night locked in each other's arms?

The questions were academic. He hadn't waited. If he had, he would have lost her anyway. Stacy would have gone home, back to Philadelphia, and forgotten all about a rancher named Royke Larson.

At least this way he had her close to him.

Draining his glass with a final long swallow, Royke set it on the tiny table with a thump. "Let's get out of here," he said decisively. At Stacy's startled glance he added, "I mean all the way out of here. It's time we went home."

Not yet three days old and her marriage was a failure! Stacy sighed as she settled back in her seat on the small plane. The only good thing that had come out of it had been

Royke's approval of her final draft of the article she'd done on Sandi.

Sandi. Stacy speculated on how Sandi would react to her and Royke's elopement.

Elopement—ha!

Smothering another sigh, Stacy opened her eyes and slid a glance at Royke's profile. Merely looking at him caused all kinds of crazy sensations inside her body! How she longed to forget herself and her worries in the haven of his arms. And how she ached for the total unity that could only come with her complete surrender to him.

Come to my room. The phrase had been revolving in her mind for three days. Would she ever feel free to do as he asked? Stacy was very much afraid that she would not. She loved him. She wanted him. But playing stand-in for another woman would destroy her spirit, and she knew it.

"What are you going to do about your things?"

Royke's sudden question startled Stacy.

"What things?"

"Your things," he growled, exasperated.

"Everything that's yours back in Philadelphia."

"Oh!" Stacy went blank for an instant; she hadn't given a moment's thought to her belongings! "I—I'm not sure. I suppose I could have mother send my stuff to me."

"When is she due back from the cruise?"

"The end of this week. Why?" Stacy suddenly felt defiant.

"You can ask her to send your things when you call her to tell her the happy news," Royke drawled not at all pleasantly.

Some happy news! Stacy kept the observation to herself. "And what about my car?" she queried.

"Have her put it in storage or sell it." He shrugged. "There are several cars at the ranch you can use."

"But none of them is mine!" she protested.

"So I'll buy you one of your own." Turning a hard-eyed glance at her, he shrugged again. "Don't make a big deal out of unimportant things, Stacy."

Subdued by the warning in his tone, Stacy bit back a retort. Well, she told herself derisively, I guess you know who plans to be the boss in this outfit! Into her mind stole a picture of her mother, leading her assorted men friends around by their noses. Apparently she lacked her mother's touch when it came to men! But then, the mere idea of any woman, even her indomitable mother, leading Royke by the nose was ludicrous!

To Stacy's amazement, once the awkward newness wore off, she settled in easily at the ranch. Like most people before her, she fell in love with Cassie Flanagan immediately. Fortunately for her, Cassie reciprocated the affection.

When informed of their marriage, Sandi and Mike were flabbergasted but delighted. Stacy's mother was stunned.

"What do you mean you're married?" she'd screamed long-distance. "Who is this Royke Larson? What do you know about him? And what shall I ever tell Bradley?"

There had been more, much more in the same vein. When at last Stacy had replaced the receiver, she was exhausted but triumphant; Virginia had agreed to send Stacy's belongings west.

Stacy's first week at the ranch was spent getting used to her new home and meeting everybody from Cassie and Matt Parker to all the ranch hands and Royke's secretary, who Stacy learned was the young wife of one of the wranglers and had her own office behind the kitchen.

It was on the Sunday at the end of that first week that Royke led her into his study. "You'll work in here," he said coolly, walking to a beautiful wood filing cabinet to pull several old ledgers out of the bottom drawer. "These are the diaries and journals I told you about." Strolling back to her, he placed them in her hands. "The complete Larson family history." A grin eased the austere lines of his face. "Every Larson, that is, except me. I'm too lazy to be bothered with keeping a diary."

Lazy? Royke! Stacy had to bite back an exclamation. In less than a week she had heard from just about every person on the property how very *un*tiring Royke was! And, of course, she'd heard it repeatedly from Sandi during her brief visit to the Case ranch.

"Do you think compiling this material into

a family chronicle will keep you out of trouble?'' he teased.

Not yet sure how to respond to this man who could switch so easily from distant stranger to teasing companion, Stacy held herself aloof. ''I never get into trouble,'' she assured him coolly, conveniently forgetting the pack of trouble she was presently in. ''And I'm positive I'll have no difficulty with the work.'' As she spoke his features hardened. Clutching the journals to her, she beat a hasty retreat, saying, ''I think I'll read over them now. If you don't mind?'' Without waiting to find out if Royke minded or not, Stacy went to her room.

Her room. Still cradling the journals to her chest, Stacy stood in the center of the large bedroom and glanced around with sad eyes. It was a lovely room, and it was hers, all hers, and she hated it. Every night she lay alone in the bed that was also all hers, and she hated that, too. After a week and a half of being Royke's wife, and sleeping alone, Stacy felt like screaming her frustration and hurt at the top of her voice. She didn't, of course. If anything, she spoke less, and more quietly, than before.

Every night Stacy lay in her bed, longing with every fiber of her being to walk out her door and along the hall to Royke's room. She knew she could lose herself there, if only for a few hours. And every night she denied herself that fulfillment.

Royke did not love her. Stacy slept alone.

The painstakingly kept records of Royke's ancestors captured Stacy's imagination from the first page she read. She was three-quarters through the second small volume when an idea wormed its way into her mind. Dismissing the idea out of hand, she kept on. Yet, the longer she read, the stronger the idea became. The information contained within the yellowed pages of the journals would make a fantastic historical novel! Especially the one kept by Royke's great-grandmother, Elizabeth, the woman who had tamed the first Royke Larson, Royke's frontiersman great-grandfather.

Yes, Elizabeth's account would make a wonderful story. In fact, it was already part of a published book!

While familiarizing herself with the room in which she would be working, Stacy had casually picked up a heavy volume that was lying on one corner of Royke's desk. At the sight of the author's name on the cover a delighted smile lit her face. That evening she pounced on Royke the minute he came in the door.

"Would you mind if I took this book to my room to read?" she asked, holding it out for his inspection.

"Dr. Dunham's book? No, of course I don't mind." Royke smiled at her without strain for the first time in nearly a week. "In fact, I was going to suggest it to you, as she included an entire chapter in it on my great-grandmother—" he paused, then added "—or did you know that?"

"No." Stacy shook her head. "But I know Jessica Dunham. I interviewed her for the magazine while she was still working on this book." Stacy smoothed her hand over the glossy dust jacket. "Dr. Dunham is a brilliant woman."

"I know. She spent a few days here while she was gathering material for her book."

With insolent deliberation Royke slowly raked her body from head to toe and back again. "Dr. Dunham is one woman who has managed to retain her femininity while asserting her individuality."

Though Stacy gasped in shock, she had no time to voice a protest as Royke continued. "Two liberated women, so alike in many ways, yet so very different in the things that count."

"What are you trying to say, Royke?" Stacy demanded angrily.

"I found Jessica Dunham brilliant, beautiful, and warm, with an innate understanding of people and their needs. I've discovered that you are merely brilliant and beautiful." As though dismissing her from further consideration, Royke spun on his booted heel and strode out of the room.

For some strange reason Stacy didn't even begin to try to understand, Royke's insult to her femininity was the spur that goaded her into trying her hand at fiction.

Once started, the work consumed Stacy. She hadn't the vaguest idea if what she was writing was any good at all, yet she couldn't stop. Using the journals but changing the names, Stacy told the story of a family that pioneered in the untouched splendor of Montana.

As the weeks of spring slipped by unnoticed, Stacy spent longer and longer hours in Royke's study pounding away at his electric typewriter.

Royke spent longer and longer hours away from home. Exhausted by the time she finally forced herself away from the machine, Stacy no longer heard him stride along the hall to his room.

By midsummer Stacy had completed a rough first draft of the manuscript and, beginning to suspect that it might actually be good, immediately began work on a final draft. Not for a second would she have listened had anyone suggested that the ten to twelve hours she spent working every day were a means of fighting the loneliness and rejection she felt.

Cassie grumbled and scolded at least once a day. Sandi called repeatedly, begging her to visit. Royke, the only person who could have reached her, grew more withdrawn with each passing week, and treated her as if she weren't there.

Two days after Labor Day, filled with nervous trepidation, Stacy mailed the original copy of the manuscript to an editor at one of the largest publishing houses in New York. Although Stacy knew there was no guarantee that the editor would like the work, she felt positive it would be read. Stacy had done a complimentary article on the editor for the magazine just prior to last Christmas.

The letdown came as soon as the manuscript was safely in the care of the U.S. postal service. Suddenly at loose ends, with nothing to do to occupy her mind and much too much time to think, Stacy began fretting about Royke's possible reaction when he discovered she had not been busily employed on his family chronicles.

Seeking diversion from her disquieting fears, Stacy suddenly became very active, taking several shopping trips with Sandi, meeting people—all of whom obviously held Royke in high esteem—writing long-overdue letters to her mother and friends, and even coaxing Cassie into letting her help with the fall housecleaning.

It was during one of the cleaning sessions that Stacy learned about Royke's rejection by both his father and mother, and the loneliness of his childhood.

"There's a very caring man behind that tough shield Royke wears," Cassie said sadly.

Up until that point Stacy had deluded herself into believing that Cassie was ignorant of their marital situation. Cassie's next words disabused her of that notion.

"I don't know what's going on between you two, and I suppose you could rightly say it's none of my business, but I love that man like he was my own, and he deserves better."

After that statement Cassie folded her arms under her ample bosom and stared directly into Stacy's shocked eyes.

"Better than me, you mean?" Stacy challenged weakly.

"I didn't say that," Cassie scolded. "And I didn't mean that, so don't you be putting words in my mouth! What I am saying is, one of you has got to make a move toward the other." Her smile revealed her wisdom. "And like it or not, I'm afraid it will have to be you."

"But why should it?" Stacy protested self-righteously. "Cassie, you don't understand the situation." Stacy paused to shake her head. "I'm not sure I understand it myself. But believe me, there is no logical reason why I should make any move at all. That is," she qualified, "unless it's back East."

"Who asked you for logic?" the older woman demanded. "I may be old but I'm surely not past the age of recognizing the symptoms of a woman in love." Stacy had the uncomfortable feeling that Cassie's still-bright eyes were boring straight into her soul. A sad smile on her lined face, Cassie continued. "Hard as it is for you young people to accept, this is still a man's world."

"Cassie!" Stacy would have said more, but the old lady forged ahead relentlessly.

"I'm not saying it's right, I'm saying it is. But the future encroaches and the man with eyes to see has noted it. So, what does he do? He digs his heels in." A compassionate twinkle lit her eyes. "In this case the heels are on well-worn boots."

"But...but..." Stacy shook her head. "I don't get the point you're trying to make."

"Why, it's simple, honey. You represent the wave of the future and, manlike, he wants *you* to come to *him*."

"But why should I?" Stacy argued heatedly.

"Because you love him."

Chapter Ten

Because you love him.

The simply worded phrase kept Stacy awake nights. Or was it the truth of the statement that did not let her sleep? Stacy had faced the reality of her love for Royke long ago. Now she plumbed the depths of that love. Was Cassie right? Was Royke waiting for her to go to him?

I won't pressure you, Stacy. When you feel you are ready, all you have to do is come to my room.

On their wedding night Stacy had taken Royke's words at face value. Now she won-

dered if Royke had meant much more than
he'd actually said.

But even if her marriage was a failure,
there was one thing that Stacy would always
be grateful for in connection with her trip
west. Through the Larson family journals and
the work of Professor Dunham, she had
gained a wealth of insight into her own sex.

What Stacy had learned was that there had
always been women of independence and individuality; what they had lacked was visi-
bility. The first Royke Larson's wife had
stood beside her man shoulder to shoulder as
he carved a home out of the wilderness. In
comparison to the rigorous existence Elizabeth Larson had led, Stacy saw that her own
life up till now had been like a pleasant outing
in perfect weather.

Stacy realized that she had based her view
of the liberated woman on her mother's example. And eventually she came to the conclusion that her mother was not in actuality
liberated, but a woman bound by the very nar-
rowness of her own fears. With sudden clarity
Stacy realized that all the control her mother
wielded, all the lovers she acquired then dis-

carded, would never free her. Only Virginia Ernshaw could free Virginia Ernshaw. No outside influence could free her.

In the end, Stacy came to the conclusion that of all the women she knew, Sandi Case was probably the most liberated. After all, Sandi had had many options to choose from, and she had made her own life. This was the woman whom Toni had condescendingly referred to as *the professional homemaker*. In Stacy's opinion, Sandi was too busy blazing her own trail along a familiar path to be bothered with somebody else's attempt to lead her in another direction.

No wonder Mike blatantly adored Sandi, for she was a real woman in the truest sense of the word. No wonder Royke loved her, too. Of course, it was this last thought that always stopped Stacy cold whenever she considered going to Royke.

Thus, her life on temporary hold, Stacy filled her hours and days with busywork. She was busy shopping, she was busy visiting, she was busy helping Cassie, and she was very, very busy avoiding a confrontation with her husband.

Four weeks after she'd mailed the manuscript to New York Stacy spent the entire day shopping with Sandi. Arriving back at the house thirty-five minutes before dinnertime, she breezed into the kitchen with a breathless "Do I have time for a quick shower?"

"Take time," Cassie replied dryly from her position at the stove. "It'll keep. Besides, Royke isn't in yet."

When was Royke ever in anymore? Stacy thought as she strode into the hall. As she went through the door, Cassie raised her voice so it would carry to the stairway.

"I put your mail on top of the desk."

"Thanks," Stacy shouted back. "I'll check it out before I jump into the shower."

Stacy never made it to the shower until the following morning.

Dashing into Royke's study, she quickly flipped through the neat pile of mail lying in the center of the desk. There were several advertisements from stores she had recently frequented, a letter from her mother, another from Toni, and the latest issue of *Women First*. It was when she lifted the magazine that Stacy noticed the message written in Cassie's precise handwriting. The message informed Stacy that Marcia Deil had called and requested that Stacy return the call.

As her eyes skimmed the note, Stacy's hands began to tremble. Marcia Deil was the editor to whom she'd sent her manuscript! Afraid to hope or even think, Stacy dialed the number Cassie had written at the bottom of the paper. It was over a half hour later that Stacy replaced the receiver.

The publishing house wanted to buy her book, *her* book! And the advance Marcia had offered had totally stunned Stacy. Of course, Marcia had cautioned, there were a few revisions they'd like done, if Stacy didn't mind. Stacy didn't. Good. Marcia had actually sounded relieved. Stacy would be receiving a contract within a few weeks.

Euphoric, not quite able to believe the conversation, Stacy was still staring at the white phone when the sound of Royke's terse message brought her down to earth.

"What, exactly, was that call all about?"

Gasping a soft "Oh," Stacy spun around to see Royke standing in the doorway, his buff-colored Stetson still pulled low over his eyes, his cotton shirt and jeans dusty from the range. He looked tired and edgy, and, somehow, rather dangerous.

"That—that was an editor," Stacy explained all in a rush. "Ah...an editor in New York," she added lamely.

"A friend of yours?" he asked tightly.

"Well, ah, not exactly a friend," Stacy stalled.

"Then what exactly?"

"Royke, there's something I have to explain to you." Stacy's mouth went bone-dry and she paused to wet her lips.

"You've accepted a new job?" he said tensely.

"Job? What?" Stacy blinked in confusion. "What are you talking about?"

"I'm asking if you've accepted a new reporting job in New York?" Royke demanded impatiently, moving into the room.

"No! Of course not. I—I...oh, hell! The editor I was speaking to works for a publishing house. They want to buy my book." There, it was out. Now all she had to do was wait for the explosion. It didn't come—at least not then.

"Book?" Royke frowned. "What book?"

Stacy bit her lip, drew a deep breath, then blurted out, "The historical novel I wrote using your family's journals as background."

There was total, terrifying silence that lasted all of thirty seconds—then the explosion came.

"You—did—what?"

Stacy swallowed against the knot of fear clogging her throat. "They're going to pay me a lot of money for it, Royke." She named the exorbitant sum in an effort to calm him down; it didn't work. In fact, Royke appeared to grow even more angry.

"You mean that all the time you spent working in here you were writing a fictionalized account of my family's records?" he asked very softly.

"Y—" Stacy swallowed again. Then, squaring her shoulders, she said quite clearly, "Yes, Royke, that's exactly what I mean."

"I see. Oh, yeah, I see perfectly."

Stacy was wondering just what he saw when he shocked her into alertness.

"Call the editor back and tell him the book is not for sale," he ordered flatly.

"It's a her...a she!" Completely flustered now, Stacy wasn't quite sure what she was saying.

"What?"

"The editor, dammit!" Stacy yelled. "The editor is a woman, and I certainly will not call her back!" Feigning an assurance she was far from feeling, she moved to the door. "I'm going to take a shower before dinner." With a cool glance she raked his dusty frame. "I suggest you do the same." With her last word she swept out the door, then ran for her room.

Stacy just wasn't quite fast enough. Royke strode into her bedroom on her heels, slamming the door behind him.

"What do you think you're doing?" Stacy gasped as he stalked across the room to where she was standing.

"Our discussion was not finished," he gritted out between tightly clenched teeth.

"Yes, it was." Lifting her head with bravado, Stacy met his glare straight on. "There's nothing you can say or do to make me call that editor."

"Really?"

The soft menace in his voice raised the tiny

hairs at the back of Stacy's neck. Hating herself for it, Stacy slowly backed away from him. Royke not only matched her step for step, he went her one better, closing the inches that separated them.

"Nothing at all?" he asked in a terrifying whisper.

"Roy-Royke?" Stacy's throat closed altogether. Wide-eyed, she watched his face draw closer and closer to hers and sensed the movement of his hands lifting to her shoulders.

Petrified, Stacy stared into his angry eyes. Yet, crazily, even as the realization of danger shuddered through her, her mind was noting the fine network of lines radiating from the corners of his eyes, the hollow look in his cheeks, the overall look of weariness about him, and she longed to touch her fingers to his face and smooth the exhaustion away.

Royke did not resort to violence. He did something much more devastating. He kissed her.

If it was meant to be a punishing kiss, it failed utterly. For an instant his mouth touched hers with gentle, featherlight pres-

sure, then, a groan rumbling deep in his
throat, he fastened his mouth to hers greedily.

All during the long hot weeks of summer
Stacy had tormented herself by wondering if
Royke was seeking release with women of the
type she had found him with that last day in
Vegas. His obvious hunger now alleviated
that particular worry. His actions spoke elo-
quently of an unbearable desire. And his need
sparked her own.

Stacy felt she was not so much being
kissed as devoured. His hard lips moved over
hers as if frantic to taste every inch of them;
his tongue searched for every hidden bit of
sweetness. His hands roamed restlessly from
her shoulders to her back, then down to the
curve of her hips to grasp and pull her tightly
to the lure of his hardening body.

The musky scent of this hardworking man
filled her senses and sent them spinning.
There had been too many long days spent at
the typewriter, too many longer nights spent
in lonely despair. This time Stacy did not
draw back.

Whimpering softly, she coiled her arms
around his strong neck and kissed him back,

matching him hunger for hunger, wanting nothing at that moment but to die in his arms.

The swiftness with which Royke removed her clothes and then his own only added to her excitement. The trappings of civilization gone, Royke became the primeval man, determined to claim what was his.

With muttered words Stacy didn't clearly hear but understood nonetheless, he told her of the richness of what he would do to her.

Writhing in his arms in a simulated battle of resistance, Stacy met and matched his gentle savagery. Nipping lightly with her teeth, clawing tenderly with her nails, she drove him to the edge of madness, which was only fair, considering that he was driving her in the same direction with his hot mouth and darting tongue and seeking, caressing hands.

It was too blazingly intense to last very long. But the blaze was beautiful and warming to the core. Shudders turned to sighs, sighs became tranquillity, tranquillity drifted into deep, fulfilled slumber.

When Stacy woke it was morning. The phone was ringing. She was alone in the bed.

Missing him, her mind muddled, aching not unpleasantly in delicate places, Stacy groaned and reached for the receiver, muttering "Hello?" when she'd finally managed to get it to her ear. The tense sound of Royke's voice brought her fully awake.

"Are you all right?"

I was till this minute. Not knowing why, Stacy suddenly felt sure Royke's absence meant bad news to follow. Still, her mind refusing to release the wonder of the night, she responded positively, if huskily.

"Yes, I'm fine." Before she could voice the one question she really didn't want to ask, yet knew she must, Royke's terse voice, lower now, sent a shaft of foreboding through her.

"I'm sorry, Stacy. I used you again, and I had no right." A soft sigh drifted along the connecting wire. "I also regret my attitude earlier in the study. I gave you the journals. You had every right to use them." His dry, humorless laugh hurt Stacy's heart. "I've just been informed that I'm behaving like an overbearing son of the prairie."

"By whom?" Stacy had to ask even

though she really didn't want to hear the answer. "Where are you, Royke?"

"The Case ranch." Stacy closed her eyes against the sudden throbbing in her temple. "And Sandi's the one who told me to grow up." His laughter this time had a hollow ring. "Of course, Sandi is the only one who could get away with telling me to grow up."

Was she expected to respond to a statement like that? Stacy wondered wearily. Apparently not, for Royke continued in a strangely tight tone. "I have an appointment in Billings later this morning. And I'll probably be late getting back." His hesitation was infinitesimal but ominous. "We must talk, Stacy. I'd appreciate it if you'd wait up for me."

Must talk reverberated alarmingly inside Stacy's pounding head. With a sinking feeling that she knew what they must talk about, Stacy gripped the receiver so tightly, her fingers went numb.

"Stacy?" Royke's sharp bark sent her teeth into her bottom lip.

"What?"

"Will you wait up for me?" he demanded impatiently.

"Yes." Stacy's whispered response carried the sound of defeat. "Yes, Royke, I'll wait up."

"Are you sure you're all right?" Now Royke's tone held a thread of anxiety. Guilt, perhaps? Stacy wondered.

"Yes, I'm fine." Just fine and dandy, Stacy added mutely as she listened to him replace the receiver.

Replacing her own receiver, Stacy flopped back onto the rumpled bed. With such an auspicious beginning, where else could a day go but downhill? Stacy knew that facing that day, and the ultimate outcome of it, would very likely be the hardest thing she'd ever had to do.

Then again, why should she bother? she mused bitterly. For all intents and purposes, last night had been their wedding night, this bed their true marriage bed. Yet, on waking next to the bride he'd so passionately made love to through most of the night, Royke had left the bed, and his bride, to go to the only person who could get away with telling him to grow up—Sandi Case, another man's wife, the woman Royke loved with his mind if never with his body.

Stifling a cry of anguish against the down pillow, Stacy felt her entire body grow hot with humiliation; she had once again played stand-in for another woman, not willingly but fervently.

Why had she allowed herself the ecstasy of full knowledge of him?

Because you love him.

Cassie's words hummed through her tired brain. Yes, I love him...and I hate myself for it!

At this point Stacy's emotions took complete control of her. I won't stay merely to be sent away! she decided irrationally. Wait up? I won't even wait out the day!

She sprang from the bed. Her movements jerky and disjointed, Stacy dragged her suitcase from the closet. A few minutes later she caught herself up short as she was about to fling another piece of clothing into the half-full valise. A sudden thought stilled her hand in midair.

Would Elizabeth Larson have run from her Royke? The answer was a resounding *no*.

Elizabeth Larson, Stacy had learned, was made of the stuff that refused to admit defeat.

Overwrought, Stacy fancied she could hear Elizabeth scolding her for her hasty actions.

So then, you're giving up, eh? Going to scoot back to the safety of Mama and the big city, are you? Throw away your chance for the good life with the only real man you've ever met—and all to soothe your silly pride! The shame of it, girl! Stiffen your back, why don't you? Meet the man halfway at least. No! Damn the pride! Go all the way if you must, but bring the man to heel, girl!

Standing irresolute at the foot of the bed, Stacy's numb fingers released their death grip on the expensive cashmere dress in her hand. The garment slid to the floor noiselessly.

Should she? Could she? *Can I?* her mind cried to the long-departed Elizabeth. But the fantasy was ended; no answers came from beyond. It was up to her, Stacy knew. But then, it had always been up to her.

Turning away from the disordered pile of clothing, Stacy walked into the bathroom. Several minutes later she walked out again, her step firm if not light. Revitalized by a quick shower, she set to work replacing the clothes she'd wildly torn from closet and dresser drawers.

When she went down to the kitchen, she found it empty. Cassie had placed a note in plain view on the kitchen table, and Stacy read it with a feeling of resignation. On the spur of the moment, apparently, Cassie had decided to travel with Royke to Billings to visit with a very dear, ailing friend of hers.

Stacy spent most of the day forgetting to eat, drifting through the rooms of the house like a restless shade. In the living room her gaze rested lovingly on the antique furniture that Elizabeth had brought west with her.

In the large dining room her hand caressed the satin-smooth, glossy cherrywood tabletop with a possessiveness she had never believed herself capable of.

In the bright many-windowed breakfast nook, where she usually breakfasted alone, Stacy sighed for the intimate, first meals of the day that might have been.

Trailing dejectedly up the stairs, Stacy avoided her bedroom and the bittersweet memories it now held. Instead, she wandered into the study. Surrounded by the reassuring coziness of the leather-bound books, Stacy chose one and tried to lose herself within its pages, but even Professor Dunham's vividly descriptive flow of words failed to hold her restless attention entirely.

Near sunset, tired and depressed, Stacy stood hesitantly at the closed door to Royke's bedroom. She had been his wife for almost half a year, yet not once had she braved this portal.

Slowly, her heart racing, she twisted the knob and thrust the door open. The room was a reflection of the man—sparsely furnished, austere, done in colors that revealed his closeness to the earth.

Stacy's gaze skimmed the heavy solid-mahogany furniture, the wide four-poster, the two overstuffed chairs that flanked the natural-stone fireplace, and came to an abrupt stop on the dusty boots, neatly aligned, sitting against the wall next to an open clothes closet. There was no power on earth that could have stopped her hungry gaze from examining the array of work clothes and suits that hung inside.

Finally dragging her gaze away, she caught sight of the wide windows opposite the door. The breathtaking sight of the sun sinking behind the majestic purple-blue mountains drew her like a magnet.

Standing at the window, Stacy stiffened as her mind recalled vividly a thought she'd had the previous spring. A thought about Royke.

Wasn't there someone waiting for him at home? she'd wondered irritably, wanting to see the last of him. Some female someone?

A brief, shadowy smile feathered Stacy's lips. Now there was someone waiting for Royke. A very unsure, frightened female someone.

Darkness had long since claimed the mountains when the sound of the longed-for yet feared voice brought an end to Stacy's silent vigil.

"Thank you for waiting."

Closing her eyes in relief at the quiet sound of Royke's beloved voice, Stacy thought: I'd wait for you forever—no, we'll wait forever, Elizabeth and I. Smiling sadly, Stacy turned to meet her husband and her fate.

"I almost didn't," she admitted candidly.

"In fact, I had begun packing to leave you."
Squinting, Stacy strove to see him in the
darkened room. The sudden burst of light as
his hand hit the wall switch had her blinking.

"What stopped you?"

"Elizabeth stopped me." Immediately
feeling stupid for the remark, Stacy was nonetheless pleased to see him frown in perplexity.

"Elizabeth who?"

"Your Elizabeth...my Elizabeth." Suddenly exhausted, Stacy lifted her shoulders in
a careless shrug. "Your great-grand-mother."

"Stacy, are you feeling all right?" Royke
asked as he walked slowly to her.

Suddenly it was all too much for her.
"No!" she shouted. "No, I am definitely *not*
all right! I'm miserable, and scared, and, oh,
God, why didn't I run when I had the
chance?"

Stark alarm widened Royke's eyes. Taking
the final step to her, he grasped her by the
upper arms, anchoring her where she stood.

"Sta—" he began sharply and got no farther.

"No!" She was crying now and unable to

stop. "I'm sorry, Royke, truly sorry you had to settle for me. I'll do my best to be a good wife to you. I can't do any more than that."

"I never asked for any more than that," Royke inserted when she paused for breath. "And what do you mean by my having to *settle* for you?" he rasped, shaking her shoulders lightly.

Stacy hesitated, drew a deep breath, then plunged on recklessly.

"Do you love Sandi?"

"Of course I love Sandi, everybody knows that." He frowned. "But what in hell has that to do with us?"

Unable to believe she'd heard him correctly, Stacy stared at him openmouthed. "What has it to do..." Her voice trailed away. "You dare to admit you're in love with another woman and then have the gall to ask what it has to do with us? Are you totally mad?" she exclaimed.

"In love with!" Royke looked thunderstruck. "In love with?" His hands gripped her arms painfully and he boomed, "I'm not *in* love with Sandi, you nit! I love Sandi like the sister I never had! I am *in* love with you!"

His face twisted in a grimace quite like pain. "Although heaven knows I wish I were not."

"Why?" Stacy asked tremulously, shivering with the feeling of hope growing inside.

"Why?" Royke repeated as if stunned. "Because I'm not a masochist, that's why. Tell me you're not going to take the money the *big* publishing house is paying you and shake the dust of this place from your shoes!"

"Is *that* why you were so upset yesterday? You believed that's what I'd do?" The hope was now singing through Stacy, still she had to be sure.

"Certainly." He bit the word off harshly. "Did you really think I objected to your use of the journals?" Before she could squeak a reply, he continued much more softly. "You can't possibly know how proud I am of you, and of the fact that you were inspired by my family's history. You drove yourself so hard all summer."

"That wasn't the only reason for driving myself, Royke," Stacy admitted baldly.

"Yes, I know." Royke's smile was self-mocking. "You were hell-bent on a means of getting away from me. Right?"

"Wrong." Stacy savored his startled expression a moment before deciding to put him, and herself, out of misery. "I *drove* myself in an attempt to blank out my longing for you."

"Stacy." Royke drew out her name as though it hurt him to say it. "You'd better mean what I think you mean," he warned her in a revealingly shaky voice.

"I mean," she said succinctly, "that I have no intention of taking the money and shaking the dust of this place from my shoes. I'll sign the check over to you, if you wish," she offered expansively. "All I want in return is for you to say you love me again."

The pressure on her arms eased as he loosened his fingers. His face softened into lines of tenderness. "I'll tell you if you'll tell me first."

"I love you, Royke Larson," Stacy said clearly. "I did on the day you made your stupid proposal." A roar of laughter erupted from his throat and Stacy demanded indignantly, "What is so very funny about that?"

"Nothing, darling." Dipping his head, Royke kissed her lingeringly, hungrily. "It's merely ironic, that's all. For you see, love, I was in love with you the day I made my stupid proposal, too."

"Oh, Royke!" Stacy moaned despairingly. "I could just hit you!"

"Oh, Stacy!" Royke mimicked gently. "I could just love you!" Drawing her into his arms, he nipped deliciously at her earlobe. "Come to bed and I'll demonstrate how much."

In the background were the sounds of Royke's and the bellboy's voices, but Stacy ignored them as she sent a pensive gaze over the hotel room. It had been redecorated since she'd last stood in almost this exact same spot. If possible, it was even more gaudy.

Had Stacy been doing an article on it, she would have described the setting as lurid, the colors suggestive. Of course, Stacy was not doing an article, had not in fact filed a report in a very long time.

The door closed quietly behind the bellboy and a strong arm slid around her waist. Leaning back against the solid muscularity of Royke's body, Stacy closed her eyes and breathed in his exciting scent.

"This room is positively wicked, isn't it?" he observed close to her ear, his moist, warm breath tickling her skin.

"Wickedly expensive!" Stacy could barely breathe let alone speak.

"Don't worry about it, sweetheart." Royke's low tone held laughter. "My wife is a very successful, very rich author."

Shifting around, Stacy curled her arms around his neck and widened her eyes innocently. "What if she finds out about this tryst?"

"Not to worry," he whispered conspiratorially. "My wife has a deadline to meet, and she's always immune to everything when she's into a chapter."

A tiny frown line drew Stacy's brows together. "Royke, I'm sorry if—" A long finger against her lips silenced her protest.

"I'm only teasing, darling," Royke scolded her gently. "We're escapees, remember? Out to indulge ourselves—" he smiled sexily "—and our appetites for a whole week.'' He ran his hands the length of her spine, his smile growing blatantly sensuous when she shivered. ''Shall we start with that costly champagne over there?''

Peering around his broad shoulder, Stacy arched her brows at the bottle of Dom Perignon nestled in a bed of ice inside a silver bucket. ''When you indulge, you do it in style!'' Narrowing her eyes, she cast him a flirtatious glance. ''Had you planned on pouring that wine over my body and then lapping it up?''

''Have you gone south?'' Royke affected shock. ''That stuff's worth its weight in gold!'' His frown was anything but intimidating. ''We will drink *that* wine slowly, from glasses, *madame*.''

''Sorehead.''

Twisting out of his arms, Stacy strolled to the low table the bucket rested on, her hips undulating with invitation.

''Well, on second thought.'' Royke's voice was now slightly hoarse. ''I might be persuaded to change my mind.''

''Too late, cowboy.'' The toss of her head set Stacy's short curls bouncing. ''You had your chance. Pour the wine." She contrived to look haughty. "Into glasses, please."

"Boy! She gets an inch of success and grows a mile of bossiness!" Royke complained to the bottle he'd begun uncorking.

"And you love every minute of it," Stacy chided him complacently, accepting the glass he offered her.

"And every inch of you," Royke murmured, touching his glass to hers. "So, drink up, my sweet, I have delicious designs on your body...whether or not it's doused in wine."

Sipping the cool wine, Stacy again perused the room, noting the changes that had been made in the three years since she and Royke had first occupied it. A shiver of anticipation feathered her shoulders as her glance settled on the bed. It was still very large and circular, but now it was raised on a plushly carpeted platform, and was draped with sheer panels straight out of the *Arabian Nights*.

Royke laughed softly as his gaze followed hers. "Seems to cry out for bunches of purple grapes and naked limbs, doesn't it?" he suggested hopefully.

"We have grapes?" Stacy fluttered her lashes at him.

"Who the hell needs grapes?" Plucking the glass from her fingers, he set it and his own on the table. "Or champagne either," he growled, swinging her into his arms and walking to the bed. "I came for the naked limbs."

Their loving was hot and intense and, at times, wild. Stacy reveled in every searing kiss, every bone-crushing embrace, every soul-joining explosion.

Some twelve hours later Stacy stretched luxuriously in the wildly rumpled sheets, her arms over her head, her toes pointing at the far wall as she worked the pleasant ache from her muscles.

"Keep that up and you're in big trouble, honey."

Provocatively curling her arms around her head, Stacy turned to gaze lovingly at her husband, her breath catching at the gentle curve of his lips, the tender softness of his gaze.

"I really shouldn't be here," she said absently, her eyes roaming over the harshly attractive, angular planes of his face. The vision blurred as Royke jackknifed to a sitting position.

"I thought we'd settled this argument before we left home," he growled, bending over her. "Dammit, Stace, we both needed this time together and you know it!"

"I know, but..." Biting her lip, Stacy let her objection trail way. "Oh, Royke," she sighed. "I miss him already."

"I know, love." Bending lower, he brushed her lips with his own. "But you've been with him almost constantly for the last two years. Good grief! You kept his cradle by your desk while you worked in the study, and you kept his crib by our bed until he was eight months old! You've barely let that boy out of your sight, while still managing to complete the Larson family chronicles *and* your second bestselling historical novel." Royke shook his head in amazement. "You've earned an enormous amount of money, but you've barely spent a dime."

"I didn't have to," Stacy inserted smugly. "You keep me very comfortably."

"That isn't the point!" Royke chided her.

"You needed a vacation. So did I." A spark of desire ignited a tiny flame in his dark eyes. "And I needed you—without interruptions."

"You haven't been doing too badly up till now." Uncurling one arm from around her head, Stacy lowered her hand to smooth it over the slight rise of her belly. Her action drew Royke's eyes, and a soft smile curved his lips.

"This one had better be a girl," he warned her teasingly. "I adore our son, the little devil, but I want a girl this time."

"Let's call and talk to R.D., Royke," Stacy pleaded.

"At three-thirty in the morning?" Royke raised one brow sardonically. "I'm sure Sandi would just love us for that." But he relented when Stacy sighed. "Stacy, love, you know R.D. is having the time of his life with Sandi and Mike. And those Case kids are probably spoiling him rotten. But, if it will make you feel better, we'll call in the morning...at a respectable hour."

"You're sooo good to me." Snuggling closer to his hard body, Stacy kissed his hairy chest. "Whatever can I do to repay you?" she murmured innocently, flicking her tongue over his nipple and smiling secretly at his sharply indrawn breath.

"Call room service and ask if they have any purple grapes."

* * * * *

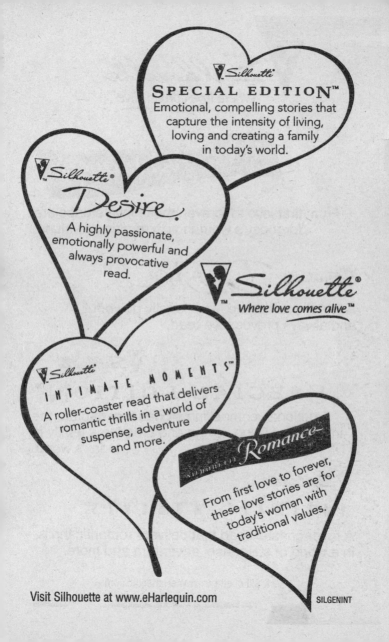

Where love comes alive™

From first love to forever, these love stories are
for today's woman with traditional values.

A highly passionate, emotionally powerful
and always provocative read.

SPECIAL EDITION™

Emotional, compelling stories that capture the
intensity of living, loving and creating a family in
today's world.

INTIMATE MOMENTS™

A roller-coaster read that delivers romantic thrills
in a world of suspense, adventure and more.

Visit Silhouette at www.eHarlequin.com